The Adventures of a Cancer Maverick

by

Nina Joy

This book is dedicated to my mum, Margaret Morton.

Although she is no longer with us, her spirit, courage and sheer zest for life continue to inspire me.

Love you, Mum.

Contents

Chapter 1 – 'Yes, this is definitely cancer'

It happened in the bathroom. I remember it clearly, as if it were yesterday. I got out of the bath and was wearing a great big, fluffy bath towel, like Superman's cape. And then I was rubbing it backwards and forwards between my shoulder blades. Don't you just love that feeling? Like having your back scratched. That's when I noticed it, in the mirror. My nipples had always been a rather fetching, matching pair. But not anymore. Strangely, my right nipple was hiding: inverted, I believe is the correct term. I had a sinking feeling in my stomach. It just did not look 'normal'. I instinctively knew something was majorly wrong. My words were not quite that profound. What I actually said was "Oh, shit!" Time to go to the doctors.

Life's funny sometimes, isn't it? Just as I was ready to book my appointment to go and see the doctor, I was taken ill. Really ill. I have never experienced such pain. A visit to the out-of-hours doctor, and I was then sent to A & E. Turns out I was having a gall bladder attack. Ouch. Not recommended. I was admitted and put onto IV antibiotics to clear the infection. I was sent home after three days to recuperate and to await a date for my op: keyhole surgery to remove my gall bladder. I was told that I was an urgent case, so hoped it wouldn't be too long. I felt that I could only face one thing at a time, so I still hadn't been to get my breast checked out. My op was scheduled for mid-July. I recovered really well and arranged to go see the doctor on 2nd August 2012.

When the receptionist asked which doctor I wanted to see, I didn't know the names of any of them. I'm never ill. Even with the gall bladder situation I hadn't needed to see a doc. So, I was booked in to see a locum doctor - can't remember her name. She was lovely, chatty, had a good bedside manner. She examined me. As well as the inverted nipple, my breast was pink-ish, and quite hot. "Cancer doesn't normally present like this," she said. That was the first time that the cancer word had entered my life. She decided to refer me to the breast clinic "to be on the safe side".

I went home and awaited the appointment letter. My appointment came through for a couple of weeks' time, on 20th August. During those two weeks I did what any sane woman does these days. I consulted Dr Google. There was lots of information to be had but no matter where I looked, the explanation for a newly-inverted nipple was not good. I had an impending sense of something serious ahead. I told a couple of my closest friends and my big sister about the referral. I thought they needed to be aware that there could be tricky times facing us.

I quite enjoyed those two weeks...when I didn't know if I had cancer, and could pretend that I didn't. It felt carefree, and I thought it may be the last time I would feel that way for a long while.

The letter about my appointment said that I should be prepared to be there a few hours. Despite offers from others to come with me, I decided to go alone. No point in two people wasting an afternoon, I thought. And no way would I get the results straightaway, so no need to worry about that.

I went armed with a book, pen and paper and prepared for the wait. When it was eventually my turn, I was called in to see a pleasant-looking male doctor. I can't remember his name, either. After a brief conversation, it was time for him to examine me, to see what the fuss was all about.

I undressed and lay on the couch. As he felt my right breast, and then my right armpit, the expression on his face changed, as if a shadow had fallen across it. I hoped he was a better doctor than poker player. I said, 'It's not good, is it?'

'No,' he answered.

'You can tell me, I need to know.'

So he did. 'This is definitely cancer.'

I couldn't believe he'd said that within the few minutes I'd been in his consulting room. He outlined what my treatment plan was likely to be: chemotherapy to reduce the tumours, a mastectomy and reconstruction, and reconstructive surgery on my healthy breast to match it to the other one; then radiotherapy, followed by five years of hormone therapy. A long route but, hey, if that's what it took to be cured. I had ultrasounds and a biopsy of the tumour in my breast. Ouch. He held up the syringe, looking at the cells he'd withdrawn. 'Ah yes, definitely cancer cells.' It seemed there was no mistake. He mentioned that it was aggressive and growing. Not words I wanted to hear. No need to wait for any results it seemed. It was a done deal.

It felt surreal. Only hours earlier, I hadn't known that I had cancer. And now I was having my future mapped out in graphic, brutal detail. I would need to come back for the 'official' results in a couple of weeks (although it all seemed a tad academic).

I left in a daze. I needed to let my sister know what was happening. And I needed to be with my people. I left the hospital and went to get the car – I recall that the seatbelt was incredibly uncomfortable against my tender breast and the dressing put on after the biopsy. It took me about an hour to get over there; all the while this new information was whirling around my head.

I shared all the information I had. There were no major outbursts. No drama - maybe the odd tear. Of course, we were shocked and sad. But other women had done it before me. If they could do it, surely I could? I was relatively young and healthy. I could do this. We could do this.

We felt the need for solidarity, to be together, so we went out for a family carvery at a local pub. And we had a jolly good night, actually. That may seem perverse but it felt absolutely the right thing to do.

I decided to be very open and honest about what I was facing, so I told friends what was going on. I knew I would need them to get me through all this. Everyone seemed to know the ropes, that chemotherapy's no walk in the park. And that I may have needed help: I had offers of cooking, shopping, ironing, lifts to the hospital and many others. Whilst all this was going on around me, I started to get my head around my new-found situation. I had numerous breast cancer and Macmillan booklets which I devoured, to get more information about what was going on with me. I like to be informed, it makes me feel more in control - even when I'm not.

Two weeks after my initial appointment I went back for the official results. My sister was with me this time. I saw a different doctor; can't remember her name, either. She had a very strong eastern

European accent, so we really had to concentrate to understand her and the unfamiliar medical jargon.

She confirmed the things I knew already plus more besides. Basically, I had a relatively large stage three, aggressive tumour which had spread to my lymph. My proposed treatment was chemo, surgery and radiotherapy. This did not make for easy listening. The prognosis was good because I was young and healthy, and the treatment was effective.

Then I had to wait to see the oncologist which gave me a chance to feel what I felt, and to calm down. Plus, we were offered a coffee. Always a good thing.

The oncologist was lovely. She answered all my questions and more. She explained the treatment she had in mind for me, but it could only be confirmed once she'd received the results of the MRI, the lymph biopsy, and she also wanted a CAT scan. She wanted to see me two weeks later to finalise the cunning plan. My words, not hers.

There was a real sense of urgency so time was of the essence, which seemed to be at odds with the two-week wait between each clinic appointment. I had originally gone to my GP on the 2nd August, and I wouldn't get my detailed treatment plan until 20th September.

It was a surreal time. It was the time of the London Olympics and Paralympics. The whole country was feeling proud and positive which I loved. Yorkshire was in a frenzy as we won more medals than the whole of Australia. Although I have absolutely no interest in sport, even I was enthralled and inspired by the Paralympics. Yet alongside this, my head was full of the cancer talk, my diary peppered with various hospital appointments and unknown medical experiences.

Once the test results were all available, I had to go back to the clinic to find out the details of my treatment plan. This was booked in for 20th September 2012. My sister, Julie, was with me for moral support, and to help me to remember what was said. I was armed with pen and paper to write down the terminology so I could later look up anything I didn't really understand. My appointment was at 4.30 p.m. It seemed like a good excuse to go out for lunch first. It was a beautiful day. We sat outside. I felt a little tense, although I couldn't have explained exactly why this was if you'd asked me. The clinic was busy, as always. It must have been about 5.30 p.m. by the time we were called in. Another new face: one of the senior consultants – a professor, in fact. I felt that I'd been upgraded, though there are times in your life when being upgraded doesn't necessarily feel like a good thing. As soon as we entered the room, you could feel the atmosphere. Like a dark cloud over us.

She started off by confirming what we already knew. 'As you know, you have a tumour in your breast and lymph. Unfortunately, the scans show that the cancer has spread to your lungs, liver and your sternum. This alters the treatment plan. We are no longer looking at a cure.'

We are no longer looking at a cure?

I would no longer need surgery; the point of the surgery was to stop the spread. That ship had sailed. The treatment would be chemotherapy to shrink the tumours and regular scans to see when they grew again, which they would. And then more chemo. And so on, until all that didn't work anymore.

Boom! It was like an unwanted explosion in my brain.

It was a total shock. <u>Not</u> what I expected to hear at all. Women survived breast cancer these days, didn't they? *Didn't they?*

In the space of a month I had gone from not knowing I had cancer to being fast-tracked to the incurable queue.

Just before the appointment ended, the chemotherapy consent form was pushed under my nose for signing. I usually read documents in detail before signing them but I really couldn't on this occasion. I was surprised I could even sign my name! I needed to get out of there, and pronto.

We left the office in silence. We got into the lift and travelled down to the ground floor in silence. It was good to feel the fresh air on my face as we emerged outside. By now it was around 6.00pm: a Thursday rush hour. The whole world needed to be somewhere: cars, busy commuters, people in a rush, chattering and traffic noise. It seemed strange that the world carried on, while my world had come to a massive full stop.

My sister asked me what I would like to do next. I didn't know. What do you do when you've just been told that you're going to die soon?

I needed to collect my thoughts, absorb what we'd just been told. To consider what and how to tell everyone. Our phones were pinging away with texts from loved ones wondering what was going on, what the news was. We went into the nearest bar – a place where I'd had many happy times - for a stiff drink and a sit down.

I felt incredibly sad. A few tears escaped, rolling quietly down my cheeks. A girl at the next table stood up to address the rest of the party at her table. She was a bride and looked absolutely beautiful. As she moved, you could see that she was pregnant. There she was, right at the beginning of such an exciting phase of her life. I appeared to be right at the end of mine.

We couldn't hide there forever. After two glasses of wine and some sisterly chat, we were ready to return those calls. You soon learn that cancer doesn't just happen to you. It happens to everyone around you. It's very hard telling the people you love that news.

From having an uncertain future, I now didn't seem to have a future at all. All the hopes and dreams I had for the future...gone.

Chapter 2 – Who am I? Patient or person?

Let's clarify what I already knew about cancer. Nothing. Zero. Zip. Nada.

No-one in my family has had cancer. No-one in my close circle has had cancer. My only experiences have involved friends of friends, or parents/grandparents of friends. Oh, and the 'breast cancer awareness' stuff that appears in every magazine each October. I didn't know the medical terminology, what the natural progression of the disease was, or the treatment options.

It was something I'd observed from a distance. Mainly on the TV. I truly was a 'Cancer Virgin'.

So, when cancer happened to me, I didn't have a frame of reference within which to place the information. It was like I'd taken the information into a vacuum, where it floated around, without context or meaning. That gave me nothing to work with. This Cancer Virgin would therefore have to passively do as she was told, in the absence of any knowledge. That was never ever going to work for me. If I couldn't navigate this situation as a Cancer Virgin, how was I going to do this thing?

Who was I before the cancer happened?

That person is still there somewhere, isn't she? I like information and knowledge, to make sense of things. I like to understand why, and what for, and what things mean. I always have done, apparently. I remember Mum telling me that I always asked "why?" when she asked me to do something or told me what to do. Not in a naughty way, but with real curiosity. I know that all children ask why, but apparently I would ask ten times instead of the usual four or five. Once I really understood why, and bought into it, I would toddle off happily to do what was asked. The need to know and to understand is absolutely hard-wired into my DNA.

Professionally, this has been incredibly useful. Most of my professional life has been spent in the financial world, working for a large bank. I have had many interesting roles over the years, all of which have involved acquiring and understanding new information, cutting through the blurb to get to the crux of the issue, assessing options, and then making decisions on what would be beneficial to the business, customers or staff. It may not sound the sexiest profession on earth but I absolutely loved it. I've worked with some brilliant people, and we've done some great work that I'm really proud of. This is my world; I spent over twenty-five years doing this type of thing. It's where I feel comfortable. It's where I belong.

As part of my working life, I've always looked for ways to improve myself, my skills and my performance.

And to share what I learned with teams I worked with. I worked in the company's training department very early on in my career, and this opened my eyes to personal development and the whole world of self-help books and courses. I was introduced to Stephen Covey and Dale Carnegie; I devoured their thoughts and ideas.

At the time, both my mum and dad worked in sales, and we often had chats over the dinner table about PMA (positive mental attitude, to the uninitiated), sharing views on training courses and books. I remember reading my dad's copy of 'Jonathan Livingston Seagull' and being totally wowed by it.

Against this background, it's not exactly surprising that I was unable to just accept the opinions of others without seeking to challenge or to verify them.

I felt that I was totally out of sync with the rest of the world on this cancer thing. Everyone else seemed to know and accept that you had chemo, that you could be ill through it, and it might not work; but everyone rallies round and you get through it. It's just what you do when you have cancer. Isn't it?

The only exception being: if you're too old or too ill or frail to face it. At which time, you choose

13

quality of life over quantity, and only then would you think of turning down chemo. To get ready to die with dignity.

That's not how I saw it at all. It all seemed bonkers to me. I felt as though, if you'd explained the treatment to an alien who'd just landed on earth, they'd think that we were some primitive life force.

Imagine it: the alien wants to know what you do for a person with a life-threatening illness, who may have some compromised organs. We tell them that we pump their body full of poison - as much poison as we think they can take but (hopefully) not enough to kill them. It destroys lots of healthy cells as well, but hey. Oh, and it will wreck their immune system, too. Yes, we know that normally your immune system helps your body heal itself from illness but that doesn't apply with cancer. Why? Well, just because. Because we want to kill the tumour, above all else.

But isn't the tumour just a symptom? What about the root cause? Why is all the effort directed at the symptom? Surely, if you don't address the cause, then this body of mine that made the tumours will just carry on doing the same? A phrase I've often used in work situations is: 'do what you always do, get what you've always got'. Seems appropriate.

Because of this, I didn't necessarily understand

the preoccupation with surgery, and cutting tumours out of the body. It may work in the short term, but if you don't address the underlying cause, surely the cancer comes back? I remember glancing at the contents of a cancer book, scanning the chapters that covered diagnosis, treatment and recovery, and on to a chapter at the end, entitled 'When the cancer comes back'. Not if. _When._ Aha! So, I was right then?

All in all, I wasn't buying this cancer business. It didn't make much sense.

Maybe this 'Cancer Virgin' was actually more of a 'Cancer Maverick'.

Amongst all this thinking, another thought came into my head. Something I'd learned of six years earlier came back to me totally unbidden. But once you know something, you can't '*un-know*' it, can you?

Six years previously, I attended a course in Manchester with several of my colleagues at that time. The course was 'Mindstore for Business', run by Jack Black. This course had a huge impact on me. There were many things I learned in those two days that changed my thinking forever.

One of them was about goal setting. Professionally, we'd always been taught to set ourselves SMART goals (specific, measureable, achievable, realistic and time-bound). Jack really

15

challenged this view; I remember him saying, 'Who leaps out of bed every morning for a realistic, achievable goal?' And he was so right! The goals that set you on fire are the stonking, unachievable ones! Wow! I set myself three big ones; I had no idea how I would achieve them but I knew I wanted those goals badly. Jack had shown me some things and inspired me to believe that I could indeed reach them.

You know what? I did achieve them. That course was pretty memorable for me. The thought that came back uninvited was regarding the time Jack mentioned he was working with someone in Germany and licensing them to use his techniques. They were going to use these techniques with cancer patients at a centre they were opening, called the 3E Centre. This thought wouldn't go away. It was knowledge that I couldn't *un-know*.

I wondered what had happened in those six years. Was the centre still around? Anything to do with Mindstore was worth looking into, I thought, particularly something that brought Mindstore and cancer patients together. With the magic of Google, I found it.

The first words on the 3E Home Page were:

'Welcome to a unique place. At the 3E Centre you will learn about the right cancer treatment available to you, and how you can take proactive

steps to put your life into your own hands.'

Wow! I felt like I had come home. To a place where they spoke my language (not German, you understand) and where the maverick in me would thrive. I read all about the Budwig quark and oil diet that they followed. I found out that they had studied cancer survivors around the world to find out what commonalities there were. I saw that they offered a five- week programme, so that you could go and learn all about this stuff before coming home and doing it all for yourself.

I felt hopeful and excited. Not feelings I had recently been accustomed to. Boy, did it feel good!

I sent an e-mail for more information and arranged to speak to one of their holistic therapists over the phone. I had a really good conversation with her and she answered my questions. I think what I really wanted was for her to tell me that they'd had someone just like me who was now cured; that I was doing the right thing. That there was proof and examples I could read about, and people who had already been there and experienced it first-hand that I could speak to. But that wasn't forthcoming. I understood why – they were very strong on ethics: they offered all the information you needed but they weren't there to persuade you that this was what you should do. Plus, we had the language difference to contend with. I asked about the 'synergetic' and 'kausanetic' treatments mentioned on the website but their explanations got a bit lost in translation, and I didn't really know what they meant.

Typically, people go for this type of treatment when all else has failed. When there is nothing more that the doctors can do. When there is nothing to lose. No risk.

I probed the idea of going to Germany with my family. They listened. They thought it sounded interesting and that I should get more information but there was a real concern that I was gambling with my life. It was unknown and far removed from anything we had come across before. I mentioned the 3E Centre to some of my friends. Generally, they said that they would support whatever I decided to do but there was some hesitation and concern hanging in the air. When I told one of my more forthright friends, he blurted, (and I quote) 'You've got to be f******* nuts!' He was really concerned about what I was contemplating. Gotta love his honesty.

This was the most difficult time for me, by far. I was coming to terms with my diagnosis, as were my family and friends. Every single bone in my body told me that the chemo route was not right for me. But not because I was ready to die - very much the opposite. I wanted to live!

My instinct told me that I should go to the 3E Centre. Yet, if anyone had asked me why, or asked for the proof, results or reasons, I'd have found it difficult to answer. At a time when I had already given the people I loved so much to worry about, I was now causing them even more concern, which was very unfair of me. But it seemed unfair to me not to.

There was also the big issue of finance to consider. The chemo/NHS route was free, whereas I would have to fund the German route. I didn't know how I would manage to do that. It was coming at a time when I was unable to turn my attention to work, and potentially wouldn't have the time or energy to work anyway. My financial future was looking extremely uncertain at best, pretty dire at worst.

I felt absolutely torn. I veered from 'yes, I must go' to 'no, I can't possibly do this', and then back again within the space of a few hours. The uncertainty was unbearable. I wished that I had never even heard about the 3E Centre and then I wouldn't have had the conflict to deal with.

Time moved at a snail's pace. By mid-September I had known for four weeks that I had cancer. And I still had no idea what I was going to do about it. The appointment for my chemo pre-assessment came through: it was booked for 4th October.

I found it impossible to decide what I needed to do. I didn't have anyone to turn to. The doctors believed in chemo, I didn't. The 3E Centre had to tread carefully and leave the decision with me. In life I've always said: if you can't decide, just do something – anything - and learn as you go along. If you change your mind, you can always do something else.

But this was different. This was literally a matter of life or death. As we headed towards the 4th October chemo appointment, the clock was ticking. Rather loudly.

Chapter 3 – To 3E or not to 3E?
That is the qvestion

I was coming to terms with the forthcoming chemo. It had been mentioned from my very first clinic appointment on the 20th August, so I'd had a few weeks to get my head around it. I had my haircut in anticipation of what was to come. My signature blonde bob became a crop. I hated how it looked. I thought I looked like a German lesbian. Not that there is anything wrong with that, if you are one. I, however, am not.

My hairdresser sister researched wigs and the styling of them. We talked about her shaving my head. I only wanted her to do it but she didn't know if she would be able to. My lovely niece sent me links to YouTube showing how you can recreate eyebrows with make-up. Gulp.

Because I had such negative views on chemo, I knew that I had to do some work on my attitude. I decided what I would visualise whilst on the IV drip: I would imagine that the liquid was an elixir for life and just what my body needed at that point in time.

My mental preparations were going pretty well. That is, until I was fast-tracked to the incurable section. It was one thing to endure chemotherapy when the ultimate aim was being clear of cancer but quite another when even the people who believe in chemotherapy tell you that it's not a cure. Once I knew that, everything changed.

To help me come to terms with my diagnosis I put my thoughts down on paper, in an online journal. To give you a glimpse as to how I was feeling, let me share with you some actual entries:

Thursday 20th September 2012 – *aka the day that changed my life.*

'Hope that doesn't sound too dramatic, because that is just how it felt. Not that I knew that in the morning… was busy with stuff as usual. Ran out of time to go through all the cancer booklets in detail. Had intended to, so that I could have the longest list of challenging questions. Julie arrived, and we went over to Lakeside Café for a sandwich before going to town. Parked in The Light because didn't know how long we would be. Appointment was 4.15pm. Not sure what time we were actually called in...might have been 5.15? Got upgraded from Dr Choudry to one of the head honchos.

The news is – the tumour is larger than they guessed and it has spread… to my lymph glands, to my lungs, to my liver, to my sternum… think I stopped listening then. While her mouth was moving, I could hear the verdict: 'riddled with it', 'game over', and 'dead woman walking'.

The treatment plan therefore changes, as 'a cure is no longer possible'. No point in surgery and the only plan is – let's guess – chemo. The only thing they've got, really. And then Tamoxifen. The best case scenario is: it would shrink and/or stop the tumours and give me a couple of years. Now that did shock me – it's not long, is it? I would be monitored every three months and at any sign of more growth: a further dose of chemo. This may carry on working. There may be a resistance to chemo over time. There may not.

Have to say, I'm not liking the sound of that. Feel very definite that I will not be doing that time after time. Chemo once, and then off to Germany, methinks. Even Julie said as much as we left the appointment.

The doc apologised for giving me such bad news. She was very professional and factual, and it went as well as it possibly could. Julie and I were outwardly calm but it's a huge shock. Worse than we expected. I talked to the doc about alternatives and she was as positive as she could be without endorsing anything. She told me about the statistician she had treated: he said that he intended to be on the longest surviving tail end of the distribution curve – and guess what, of course, he was. The tail end of the curve was in about

23

four years' time, though. She therefore believes that people who take an active interest and participation in their treatment are the most successful. She asked that I tell her about anything I do so that they can be aware of any issues with the conventional treatment.

When we came out, although outwardly calm, I felt utterly churned up inside. Decided to call off for a drink and as we were outside Browns, this seemed the obvious place. Julie had coffee, I had a whacking glass of wine which was delicious. Ironically, I found I was sitting back to back with a bride; she looked beautiful and when she stood up, we saw she was pregnant. There she was: at the beginning of a very exciting phase in her life. And here I was: apparently, at the end of mine. The pianist was tinkling on the ivories and I commented that it would be a great scene in a film. Wendy was texting for news, as was Lucie. I made Julie go out and ring her. Poor Juice. I didn't have this amount of crap to deal with when I was her age. After one for the road, Julie took me home. I had a long conversation with Wendy.

Don't think I slept very well.

Friday 21st September

Only a month since I found out for certain that I had cancer and I've already been fast-tracked to the 'incurable' queue. Bugger.

24

It came to me overnight: why am I even bothering with chemo? I hate the idea and even they have said it can't cure me. Not much of a risk to turn that down... is it?

Had coffee with Jane; she picked me up and we went to Café Istanbul. I had sent a text to warn her it wasn't great news but she seemed extraordinarily light... I don't think she understood. Explained over coffee. Think she gets it now. We were both a bit emotional.

Didn't quite know what to do with myself when I got home... Needed a hug so I rang B. He is going to come over after work.

Then, I got into action mode. Looking back at all the info on Germany in the light of this new situation. Had a consultation with Klaus from the 3E Centre. It seems that whilst I didn't feel able to go this route before, I now have little to lose and everything to gain.

In many ways, it feels like this is my destiny. To be unconventional. Not many people are in my situation where they have the freedom to be maverick about this. I can - although I would like to do it with Julie, Lucie and Dad giving me their blessing.

My chemo appointment letter came: it's booked for 5ᵗʰ October, so I put it in the diary. For now.

B eventually arrived – was nice to see him. We

eventually talked about what's going on. He was in shock, I think, and just can't believe it.

Saturday 22nd September

Feeling much, much calmer again today. Arranged to see Sue for lunch. It's a beautiful sunny day, so where better than Napa? Went up there early... sat outside with my notebook and worked through how I'm feeling about all this. There are many reasons why I truly believe that Germany is my destiny. I didn't want surgery – not having it. Didn't want chemo; as it can't cure me anyway, doesn't seem quite so bonkers. Definitely don't want multiple chemo over the coming years, so why not start as I mean to go on?

Had arranged to meet with Julie and Lucie. Lucie didn't look quite herself – very puffy eyed. Turns out she has cried a lot, including four times at work yesterday, and she couldn't eat anything until 7p.m. She and Katie have been planning fundraising and allsorts by the sounds of it.

I didn't handle telling Julie that I don't want to do chemo very well; I just blurted it out which was a bit mean – she said she felt like it was Thursday all over again. I'm really sorry for having done that.

We discussed things a bit more – Lucie shook her head at me being a bit of a rebel and Julie wonders what she has done to deserve me. Oops.

Had a shopping frenzy: got five beautiful new dresses, a skirt and a top! Feel very spoiled. I like.

Went home; it was about 7.30 when I got there. Had a nice night: tea, TV and Twitter.

Sunday 23rd September

Awoke too early, 4.30ish. Did some bits and pieces and had another snooze. Couldn't decide which dress to wear; what a lovely dilemma.

Went over to Julie's. David was a bit upset. James says he thinks Germany is a great idea, which I liked. Julie and Lucie arrived home; they seem more accepting of my plan. Went to Whiteleys for afternoon tea which I really enjoyed. We had some more cancer chat – am inspired to know that the tumour Oscar Dog had round his kidneys and liver has disappeared, and the only "treatment" he had was a change of food, and small portions of it. Who knew that Oscar Dog would be inspirational?!

Monday 24th September

Went round to work alongside Jane – it's such a horrid, dismal, rainy day, I was glad that I did. Started with the 3E health questionnaire so it was good to have company. They ask some amazing questions – definitely holistic in the true sense: all about the person. Moved on to flights – booked my outward one. Then

27

it was time to go over to Dad. Julie was there which I'm pleased about. Told dad what had happened and what I was going to do about it. He wished that he could have the cancer for me. But I said that I'm in much better condition to sort it. He obviously was upset but he listened and thanked me for being honest with him. I think he needs to digest the information, and he'll probably have more questions for me next time I see him.

Got a call from my breast care nurse: told her that I'm not going to do chemo. She thinks I should talk to another senior consultant. Not sure…not if he is going to just talk me into chemo.

Back home. Felt really tired, not sure why? All this emotional stuff, maybe. Had a snooze before getting spruced up to meet Paul at Napa. We had a good evening but inevitably it was cancer chat and my mission. Paul is with me and he is going to tell Gill for me.

Tuesday 25th[h] September

Working at home today; nothing planned for this evening. Need to make progress. Finished the health questionnaire and got that sent off. Got quite cross about an email from breast care nurse: Dr Tim, senior consultant, thinks there is some merit in me taking Tamoxifen, even if I'm not doing chemo. Googled some info. Apparently, Tamoxifen can shrink/stop tumours by blocking oestrogen. Why was this not discussed with me when I was so vociferous about chemo, and when asking about my options??!!! Contacted Germany for their opinion: they said 'take it', if my doctor and I think so, but they would choose I3C. Got that instead; if I'm putting myself in their hands, may as well do so wholeheartedly. Had some emails from Kimm and have booked a session with her on 4th October; she also had some lovely words for me and some recommendations that I have acted on. Had a surprise phone call from Simon asking if I was doing anything this evening... well, I am now. What a lovely surprise. Gave me a boost and I got more done during the day. Simon came and we had coffee and lots of chat before going up to Napa. A lovely evening; got a very big hug before he left.

Wednesday 26th September

Well, this is a first: a session with a healer. But, hey, I've got to cure cancer - so any help from any source is fine by me. Didn't really feel much rapport with her to start with… and my sceptical side was a bit twitchy when she was talking about geopathic stress… but I will take it on board. Really enjoyed the session and didn't want it to end. Felt all light and weightless and pain free. Lovely. Went home and got busy again, booking flights, and ordering the EHIC, etc.

Thursday 27ᵗʰ September

Work, plus dinner and drinkies. A great day.

Friday 28ᵗʰ September

Felt a bit hungover but it was good to just go a bit mad and forget.

The letter from the hospital with my full written diagnosis arrived. Couldn't read it. Gulp. Also got bone scan appointment from the NUCLEAR MEDICINE DEPARTMENT. I kid you not!! I'm not surprised cancer patients die; they do their best to scare the bejesus out of us.

Went up to Napa in the evening for a drink with Jane – had a good old chat. She is now convinced that this is the right choice for me. So is Wendy. Actually, most of my friends think that this is all very 'me' – I have always done things differently, so why not now?

Saturday 29ᵗʰ September

Couldn't get going; felt a bit down. So, got all spruced up, new dress on and contacted Rita - went over there. She is just fabulous. Had a good old chinwag, and coffee and biscuits. She read my full diagnosis letter for me. So, now I don't need to. We talked about my German adventure, my book and my legacy – but not because I'm going anywhere, just 'cos it's exciting! Glad I went out, can now be chilled being home alone this eve.

Sunday 30th September

Had a leisurely start to the day and got all spruced up to go over and meet Julie H at the Black Horse. We had a lovely time. Julie found the latest news quite hard to take but we talked through it. Talked about Sharm, and going again. Boy, would I like that. Met up with Julie and the gang, then on to see Dad and back to Julie's for tea.

Monday 1st October

Felt a bit 'so-so' today.

Tuesday 2nd October

Needed to go down to hospital to pick up my medical records. Gulp. Jane was kind enough to take me to Jimmy's; just a quick errand, didn't have to make a meal of it. Then off to Harrogate for hypnotherapy. It went really well, visualising destroying the cancer cells in my body, James Bond style. Thought my subconscious should know that we can do this.

Wednesday 3rd October

Picked G up at the station; didn't really know what to expect but he has always had this healing thing, so why not? I did deep breathing to relax and then his hands hovered over my body; it was like being under a heated lamp – amazing. I also felt really strange feelings in my body. At one point I felt quite emotional

31

and more of a connection with Mum than I have done through this. Went to Lakeside Café for lunch, and then back for one more session.   Dropped him off at the station then scooted over to the Trafford Centre to see Joe. It was sooo good to see him. It was hard for him to hear what's going on but we got there in the end. Indulged in our usual giggling and outrageousness.

He treated me to my meal then we stopped off at Selfridges for him to have his eyebrows threaded. How wonderfully gay is that?!

Thursday 4th October

Today is the day I should have been going for my chemo pre-assessment. Decided to go public on Twitter and tell all my gang. Got some great messages, lots of resources and info, and feel it's the right thing to do for me. Just need to get my blog up and running

I've been in quite a lot of pain these last few days; not only does it hurt but then I start to feel that things are happening. It must be spreading like wildfire. And because it hurts, I can't forget about it for a single second. Replying to messages, etc. took up more time than I thought but got some brilliant replies from all sorts of people, and many hugs. Sophie (who I only know from Twitter) got in touch: she cured herself of ovarian cancer in 1995 without chemo. How inspirational is that?! Went for my session with Kimm at 'The Happiness Centre'; not sure what to expect but looking forward to it nevertheless. Sophie was having a session with her earlier (total coincidence!) and hung around to say hi, which was lovely.

The session with Kimm was amazing, really – she totally gets me, and everything she said reinforces my own thoughts on what is going on. That I have been training for this all my life. This is what I'm here for: it is life changing. Perversely for my circumstances, the overriding thing she got from reading me is excitement. Eventually, I laid down for the healing. It was a really pleasant experience – apart from the immense pain as I lay down – it felt like I had an elephant sitting on, and crushing, my very tender breastbone. Ouch. Came away feeling that I had enjoyed it and very calm and happy to have the reinforcement of my thoughts.

Dashed to meet Laurane and Jackie at Napa. We had a lovely evening and giggled a lot. But the pain was getting to me and I was quite pleased to leave and come home to bed. Even took some painkillers…

Friday 5th October 2012

This is the day I should be having my first chemo session.

As I was woke, I began to realise that the pain wasn't

there...Felt a really strange sensation in my right breast – as if there was something fizzing inside. All I could visualise was an Alka Seltzer tablet fizzing away and dissolving! Now, that's an exciting thought. I got up – still no pain. Wow. I wouldn't have believed anything could happen that quickly! Feel better than I have done for ages.

Realised, now that my breast and sternum aren't as painful, that my shoulders and neck are in absolute knots. Rang up and got a physio appointment. She really worked my shoulders which is what they needed but it made me feel a bit sick and tired afterwards. Had a lay down with a hot water bottle.

Feeling in a really great place. Home alone in the evening but lots of chat on Twitter to support me, and on Facebook, my friends are calling themselves 'Team Nina'. Need a long bath, to do some of my paperwork and get ready for work tomorrow. It's all good.

Saturday 6th October

Feel at a bit of a loose end. Was supposed to be seeing B tomorrow; he sent me a text asking if we could make it next Sunday instead - the day I'm setting off for Germany! Doh. Really upset me – shows how much he doesn't understand about all this stuff. That's that then. I might see him when I get back. Or not.

Sunday 7th October

Went over to see Dad. He asked more questions but all relatively okay. Then went to meet the gang at Whiteleys which was good. Julie was definitely more chatty, which I liked. Went back to theirs for a bit. David will be at camp next weekend so he said his goodbyes which made me gulp. Then home, feeling good and optimistic.

Monday 8th October

Started the day at Jane's, working through my list. Couldn't find the info sheet from Germany and various other things. Maybe I haven't been as calm and clear thinking as I thought I had.

Asked for it to be re-sent. Did a few other things and was fine, until I started ringing round for travel insurance. I don't seem to be insurable – because I'm not having chemo (yes really!), and haven't got a track record of lots of doctors' reports due to being so recently diagnosed. Generally feel like a dead woman walking. Felt a bit upset, so glad I was going to meet Julie at Pudsey. Had a great time; Julie was the best shoe shop assistant ever: pair of boots, shoe boots, and shoes, plus trousers and a skirt. Think that should just about do it. Enjoyed it immensely.

Had to dash home as going to Harrogate Theatre to see a comedian with Jane, Debbie and Sara. No time for any tea. It was good but seats were most uncomfortable and lop-sided! Was really tired but couldn't get to sleep straightaway. Guess I shouldn't have packed quite so much into my day.

Tuesday 9th October

The boiler was off, so had to wait for hot water. Felt tired and had no time for a bath due to boiler. Not a good start to my day.

Jane and Sara have hatched a plan to make the Germany trip more fun for me – Jane is to come out with me for a couple of days and Sara will pay for it! My initial reaction was to say no – but when I had enough money, I would have paid for that sort of thing in a heartbeat. And they offered. And it will make it more of an adventure, so that I arrive in good spirits. I said that if she could get on the flight, it was a yes. And she could, so we will sort it out tomorrow.

Spent the day with Lee; not home until 7.30. Tired… and I've got another full-ish day tomorrow... But Jane helping me with prep tomorrow, and I have tomorrow eve, all Thurs and all Fri, so will be fine. Aaaaaaaaaaaand...........................breathe.

****

It's an interesting period to look back on. Going from despair to action; from uncertainty to certainty. And being open to learning lots of new things. I had never even considered healing before yet here I was, having three sessions in a short space of time.

It looks as though I made my decision very quickly, doesn't it? But bear in mind that ever since I found I had cancer, on the 20th August, I had toyed with the idea of going to the 3E Centre. In light of this new information it just made utterly perfect sense. Having made the decision it felt like the most massive weight was lifted from my shoulders. I could get into action mode.

I needed to plan being away for five whole weeks. I was booked to go out on Sunday 14th October, so I had about three weeks to get sorted. There were flights to book and travel arrangements at the other end. And packing to think about....what to take? The Centre suggested comfortable clothing and walking boots! Not really what you'd find in my wardrobe, it has to be said. I decided to ignore those instructions. Everyone else could slob around in trackies if they wanted, but I wouldn't be. And, of course, there was the small matter of how to fund the trip. I decided not to get too concerned about finances at this point. I would put it on a credit card for now, and decide what to do about it on my return.

Travelling is something I have done lots of, much of it on my own when away on business. So, you would think I would be fine hopping over to Deutschland, wouldn't you? Not so. There is something about being told you have cancer that makes you feel very vulnerable. Plus, I was physically feeling a bit on the delicate side. It was good to have a friend travelling with me. My sister took us both to Manchester Airport and I felt quite emotional as I said goodbye.

Because the 3E Centre is something of a retreat, connection with the outside world is limited. There was only one computer in the building, no wi-fi, no television, and it was touch and go if you got a mobile phone signal. Team Nina was right with me, and they wanted to know what was happening - and I certainly needed to communicate with them. Clearly, this would not be possible on an individual basis. I therefore started a blog, so that one update would help everyone keep tabs on me. Much as I wanted to concentrate solely on the job in hand, I needed that lifeline and support.

I felt very lucky that I had been able to drop everything and go. It felt like it was my destiny; I was meant to know about it - I was meant to go there. The German adventure began.

Chapter 4 – My German adventure

It was Monday 15th October 2012. The taxi took us up the hill to the 3E Zentrum. I had seen pictures on the website so I recognised the building as we pulled into the drive. Not the prettiest place I've ever seen. The word 'functional' sprang to mind. I felt as though I had been sent away to boarding school for being naughty and getting cancer.

Once inside, it felt more welcoming. It wasn't so much hotel, more training centre - with a touch of Ikea-chic. Elke, one of the holistic therapists, introduced herself and showed me to my room. Should I have been concerned that I was in room 13?

I unpacked and settled in before going down to the communal dining room for lunch, hovering nervously at the door to see what was what. Where to sit? There seemed to be an established order of things. It became apparent that the German speakers were on one long table. The English speakers at the smaller table welcomed us. They were all there as couples, from Canada; Tel Aviv; Houston, Texas; and Brighton. An eclectic mix to say the least. A group which would never ever have come together in normal circumstances. The one thing we did have in common was cancer. We got the cancer chat over with quickly: who had what, where and for how long.

The starter was a salad buffet, vegetarian bolognese and fruit with coconut quark. It was quite delicious. Everyone seemed to be helping themselves to various teas – as a confirmed coffee-lover who can't even stand the smell of tea, I approached them with trepidation. I found a relatively palatable fennel-and-something-else-I-couldn't-translate combo. Not bad. I suppose.

After lunch, we new arrivals (which was me, and the American and Canadian couples) had our introductory session. We were talked through the 3Es that represent the three key parts of the regime - the 3E version of the three aspects cancer survivors around the world turn their attention to:

- Eat well: fresh vegetarian food, following the Budwig diet protocol

- Eliminating toxins: take less into your body, and get more out

- And, most important of all: Energy; positive thoughts and focus, purpose love and happiness

We learned about the daily schedule which had been devised to build all those things in as daily and weekly habits. We were introduced to one of the habits straightaway: we were given our enema kit and guidance on how to do the daily coffee enema. Yet another first. So, I wasn't quite giving up coffee then?

I had time in my room that afternoon – navigating how to tackle my very first coffee enema. I felt strangely proud that I could do it. And it was nowhere near as bad as I'd imagined.

I made the important discovery that I had enough signal to send and receive texts. It's hard to explain how happy this made me. I also had time for a bit of reading and a small snooze before tea at 6pm, sharp.

Salad, homemade soup, with rice cakes and a little cheese. Nice.

After eating, I went to the library to see if I could have a dabble on the computer. This was to be my lifeline to the outside world and to home: my blog. I needed to be sure I could access it. I found that Lucie had done a blog post, which brought a lump to my throat.

My sister had given me a Winnie the Pooh notebook, and I used this to start my daily journal, capturing what happened and what I thought each day.

The entry for Monday 15th November 2013

finishes with:

What a great first day. I already have a sense of what a brilliant choice this was. Now, when I'm here, it seems the accepted obvious way. No-one even talks about if or whether it will cure. They, we, all just know and trust and believe that it will.

It occurred to me that cancer wasn't the only thing we had in common at all. We had all chosen to come here. To do what it took to get well, to learn and to change. It felt good to be surrounded by like-minded people for the first time.

Tuesday was a big day – my first full day at boarding school, and the day Jane went home. Let me tell you about the daily schedule. As the polar opposite of a creature of habit, this was something of a culture shock.

DAILY SCHEDULE

7.00am: Down to the dining room for "Swish and go" (oil-pulling), and glass of sauerkraut juice

8.00am: Breakfast. Quark and oil mixture, plus ground flaxseeds, nuts and fresh fruit. Tea and water

Between 9.00am and 12.00 noon: Various classes, group or one-to-one

10.00am: Collect fresh vegetable juice from the dining

room

12.00 noon: Lunchtime. Salad buffet, warm vegetarian dish, quark and oil dessert

Walk – classes schedule permitting

Between 1.00pm – 5.00pm: Various classes, group or one-to-one

3.00pm: Collect papaya juice from dining room

6.00pm: Supper. Salad buffet, fresh soup, rice cakes and cheese

This schedule became the backbone of each day. There were many regular things to fit in around it, plus scheduled classes. Our own personal schedule was given to us at the beginning of every week.

Tuesday 16th October

My first morning was challenging: the oil pulling was okay, I suppose - if you like the feel of sunflower oil in your mouth. But the sauerkraut juice? Hmmm. Let's consider what sauerkraut is: fermented cabbage. Aka rotting cabbage. Which is what it smelt and tasted like. I did actually manage to get it down. It helped to keep saying to myself: 'it's better than chemo; it's better than chemo'…

Had meetings with the holistic therapist and

the doctor so that my personal 'prescription' for my stay could be decided.   The holistic therapist was called Christa. She'd had breast cancer herself, so she knew how this all felt.   We went through my health questionnaire and she asked lots more questions. I was to get my treatment plan on Friday.   I hoped it was stupendous!

I then had time to sit in the sun and do some journalling until lunchtime. Straight after lunch the taxi arrived for Jane and I waved her off. I felt very alone. Ah, yes, that's because I was. Alone in a strange place where I didn't understand the language. Where all the English-speaking crew were in couples, and who were twenty or thirty years older than me. Where there were no familiar places or people, or even things, such as a car or TV. Weird.   The boarding school feeling came over me again.

Time for my appointment with the doctor. He was brutally honest. He suggested that with chemo my chances of five-year survival were about 4%.   My chances by doing this? Hard to say, but perhaps 50%. He said that in my position he would be doing the same. To add a dose of realism, he reminded me that I was in 'grave danger'. He said to see what could be done in five weeks, and that there were some other avenues to pursue if need be. He told me about a doctor in Munich who delivered targeted chemo which was much less invasive. It was a good meeting, but also sobering. This was clearly not a walk in the park.

After that I had an hour of reflexology. Totally relaxing! Then I did my enema and had a little snooze before supper.

Supper was fine, with lots of chat. Afterwards, I tried to get on the computer but it was occupied. Everyone else had retired to their rooms so I did the same. I read, had a bicarbonate of soda bath, and then to bed. Felt a bit tearful. Not sure why. Maybe I'd had some emotions stored in my feet and they'd been 'reflexoligised' out?

Wednesday 17th October

Managed to get the sauerkraut juice down in one. Had a group session with Klaus in the morning - he of Mindstore Germany fame. This I liked. We started to explore some challenging questions – why did I get cancer? What needed to stop in my life? What needed to change? Difficult topics to face up to. But I would, while I was there.

I went to pay my bill. I held my breath while the credit card machine made its whirring noise... Phew. It went through. Good job I'm worth it.

After lunch, I had Darkfield Analysis on my schedule. Something to do with blood, apparently.

The nice man took a bit of my blood and then showed me on the computer what it looked like, compared with what it should look like. They shouldn't have been stuck together like that, it seems – more water, the diet, and the detox will make a difference, I'm told. I'd know, as I had to have it re-done before I left.

After my papaya juice I decided to go for a walk. Everyone was waxing lyrical about how lovely the countryside was. Just looked like a lot of fields and trees to me. I'm such a heathen. Would rather have been wandering round Marks and Spencer's, if I was honest. I bumped into the Houston couple and the Tel Aviv couple. They'd found a little watering hole within walking distance and invited me for coffee and cake. Coffee and cake? I presumed it was just a turn of phrase, and I accepted the invitation. I didn't have any money on me, so I hoped someone would treat me.

It was a gorgeous little place. Very alpine chalet-esque. They did order cake! Although, of course, only one from each couple had cancer, so it was the other halves who were indulging. I ordered green tea. There was no way I was doing anything other than following exactly what I needed to do. It was a pleasant interlude. We felt relatively normal; not 'inmates'.

Time for a coffee (enema, obviously) before

supper. I felt a bit tired. I think it was because the pace was slow; it was all about relaxing with no outside distractions. The Canadian couple were in their eighties and not very computer savvy – they wanted to send an e-mail to their daughter to let her know that they were okay. I acted as secretary and did the honours. They were so grateful. It felt nice to help. I even managed to do a blog post before going to my room for bathing, journalling and sleep. I thought I'd be okay at this boarding school malarkey.

Thursday 18th October

I got more info from Mr Tel Aviv. He had colon cancer which had now spread to his lungs but he'd been living with cancer for eleven years. Mrs Houston first had breast cancer twenty-eight years ago, and she now had pancreatic cancer. It appeared that there were ways to live with cancer and still be well and happy.

Time for my first Colon Hydrotherapy. Always thought colonics were for neurotic LA types. But no; apparently, they're good for clearing the tubes of all the build up through the years from eating processed foods and the like. Not the most pleasant experience, but not so bad either. Who knew there was so much there to flush out?! Not sure why but I felt really, really tired afterwards. I slept from 10.45am to about 11.45am. Lunch was lovely – we went outside on the terrace in the sun. I stayed out there for a bit, purring like a blissful pussycat. Until it was time for my first Meditation class. Not very me but, hey, I needed to change. Did affirmations, like 'I am healthy'. I figured I'd need a bit more practice at this stuff.

Joined Mr and Mrs Houston for a walk. Had a coffee (!) when I came back, and then a quick spruce up before supper. Finished the day by checking messages on my blog and doing a bit of texting, before bathing, journalling and bed.

I was settling into the routine. If this was what I needed to do to get well, bring it on!

Friday 19th October

Found out my suggested treatment plan today. I'd do everything they recommended, including the things that cost extra, such as the vitamin C infusions. After all, that was what I was there for. Even more things to fit into the daily schedule – it felt like a full-time job!

I received my first parcel from home (thank you, Lauraney – a card, sparkly nail varnish, a bracelet and some chocolates (will give these to the Other Halves)). Plus a cat mask for Halloween. Marvellous! What more could a girl need?!

I sat outside in the sun to do my "homework"

from Klaus, on what needed to stop. I faced up to the things in my life which had been causing me stress or unhappiness. You know, those things we normally ignore or skip over, or pretend are okay.

I had my first 'Inner World' healing session with Hannelore. She was lovely. She talked to me about Mum, who had died the previous November. It made me incredibly emotional. Over dinner, I chatted to Mr and Mrs Brighton, who were due to go home the next day. Blog post then bedtime routine, which now also included a hot water bottle liver compress. It was soothing. I liked it.

At the end of the first week it was all settling into a bit of a pattern. Each day there were a number of things to fit into it, yet it was relaxing and calm and provided the mental space to think about what was happening.

Saturday 20th October

The weekends, however, were different. The staff didn't work weekends – other than the chef, of course. So, the bits of the treatment plan you could do for yourself carried on but there were no classes or treatments.

I had a very encouraging happening that morning – when I put on my deodorant, I noticed that I had a right armpit! So what, you may ask. It had been so swollen for so long, but now it actually went in as an armpit should! It felt like an early indication that the treatment worked. I told everyone about it at the dining table and they burst into a spontaneous round of applause. Everyone was really pleased for me.

We (the English speaking gang) decided to go into the nearest village, Schorndorf. It was a pretty little place, with a farmer's market and town square, and even a department store. I enjoyed wandering around, feeling normal', and stopping off for a green tea.

Feeling very giddy, we decided that we would have a day out the next day and ordered a taxi to come and pick us up early doors.

Sunday 21st October

Our taxi whisked us into Stuttgart, to the Mercedes museum. The building itself was amazing! Lots and lots of exhibits, from early prototype vehicles right up until those of present day. Some amazing ones; took lots of photos to show my bro-in-law, he'd have loved it there. I felt nervous about what to choose from the restaurant menu for lunch. I didn't want to compromise my Budwig diet, so I chose onion soup and vegetable goulash.

We went out in the sun, got out the bottles of papaya juice we'd brought and had our afternoon dose of vitamins.

Felt a tiny bit down. The schedule was a little oppressive for a free spirit like me. It was too soon to say I felt better. And the novelty had worn off for everyone at home, so I got very few texts.

Had I really only been there a week? One down, four more to go. They stretched out in front of me. The end seemed a long, long way away.

Gosh.

Chapter 5 – The German adventure continues

Week 2 – 22nd October

I felt a bit down today. I missed my life. I felt as though I'd been picked up from my normal habitat and dropped into a strange land where most people spoke a different language – and where even the ones who spoke mine were talking about things I didn't care about. The chat this morning was about pensions, grandchildren and domesticity. I desperately want to be talking about clothes, unsuitable men, make-up and sex; I wanted to giggle and to be myself. Wished I had someone to play with. Luckily, the weather was still glorious, and I could sit outside to do my homework. Sunshine always helps. My spirits were restored and I was ready to face the week.

I had more things to incorporate into the daily schedule from my personalised treatment plan. A typical day was now as follows:

> 7.15: Swish and go (oil pulling) and sauerkraut juice
>
> 8.00: Breakfast; take supplements
>
> 9.00: Exercise class

9.30: Intravenous vitamin C

10.00: Fresh juice

10.00 – 12.00: Group class e.g. Mindstore techniques, visualising, Budwig diet theory

12.00: Three course lunch; take supplements

1.00: Walk

2.00: Colon hydrotherapy

3.00: Papaya juice

3.00: Rebounder for 10 mins; inhaler for 15 mins; visualising 30 mins; homework from classes, reflecting and learning

6.00: Supper; take supplements

7.00: Blogging – if I could get on the computer!

7.30 Bedtime routine: enema 30 mins; bicarbonate of soda bath 45 mins; liver poultice, journaling and visualising.

As you can see, the days were pretty full. The timetable provided a rhythm and framework for the day and they passed quickly, punctuated with the sociability of breakfast, lunch and supper around the dining table. I really enjoyed the classes – learning all about the 3Es. I absorbed the information like a sponge.

All I had to do while there was to work on me, be open to what I learnt at the classes and, most importantly of all, figure out what to do about all this when I get home. That's when the work would really start.

By Saturday, the weather had completely changed - it snowed! We all went into Schorndorf and it looked even prettier in the snow. The town is very traditional; the shops close on a Saturday afternoon, so we returned in time for lunch. I felt a bit down in the afternoon: I was tired, not sure why, perhaps as a result of the detoxing and intensive treatments. I was in pain and I hadn't heard much from my outside world. I felt like the whole planet had gone to a party and forgot to invite me. There was more time to think about it on a weekend, as there were no classes or treatments.

Sunday was a new day. The sun made the snow twinkle and we decided to venture out for a communal walk and stop off at our local watering hole for green tea. We must have looked an interesting, mismatched bunch to those looking on.

In the afternoon, I managed to snaffle the computer to have a Skype call with my sister and her family. Just what I needed: spirits beautifully restored again.

Everyone there was at a different stage of their illness. Many didn't look ill at all. One or two definitely did, although the "rules" for attending made it clear that this was not a hospital,and there was no medical care available. Everyone needed to be self-sufficient. One girl, Claudia, was clearly unwell. She was in pain, found it difficult to eat; and if she did, had difficulty keeping it down. She came over to talk to me and Mr and Mrs Canada after supper. She looked so sad. I hugged her and she just sobbed. It made me think.... of many things. Mostly, that I was very lucky not to be in that state and to have found this treatment at the right time.

Week 3 – 29th October

Our group was now four, as Mr Houston and Mr Tel Aviv had gone home. This left me, Mrs Houston, and Mr and Mrs Canada.

The week's big news is that we were to do a liver cleanse over the following few days. I didn't really know what one was, but if it kept my liver pink and healthy then I was all for it. It was optional but I was there to do everything I could while I had chance; no way would I be opting out.

The liver cleanse meant that we had to drink apple juice and have a daily bicarb enema. This was in addition to the usual coffee enema and the twice-weekly colonics. Wow – my insides were going to be very clean and twinkly! Perhaps unsurprisingly, I felt a little drained. Literally.

The highlight of Tuesday was getting a parcel with a gift from my friend, Andy. What on earth do you send to someone who is isolated and in need of entertainment; a copy of 50 Shades of Grey, of course! When I opened it I laughed hysterically. Very tricky to explain why to the very lovely, but rather God-fearing, Mr and Mrs Canada, aged 82. Oops!

We had a cookery class with Wolfgang the chef, to learn 1001 ways to serve quark and oil. I liked Wolfgang and he could do amazing things with buckwheat. I jokingly asked if I could take him home with me. He looked a little worried and said, 'I vill haf to ask my vife'. I'll take that as a no, then.

On Halloween we made a special effort at dinner. Mrs Houston wore a black t-shirt with a twinkly orange pumpkin on it. I wore my cat mask…as you do. The German contingent was amused and confused in equal measure. Us four liked it, though.

Weekend arrived again - no classes, no staff around. Must have been Schorndorf time. I found a gorgeous jewellers and bought myself souvenir earrings. Sparkly earrings are very good for people with cancer. Obviously.

On Sunday, we ventured further afield, to a place recommended by one of the therapists: Besigheim. It was absolutely delightful. Everything a German village should be. It was lovely to be out and about. We went on to Ludwigsburg, which has a beautiful Versailles-style palace and enjoy wandering round, being touristy.

No need to rush back for supper, as the next phase of the cleanse was fasting. I could still drink my fennel tea, though, which I was becoming rather partial to. Amazing how your taste buds adapt, isn't it?

Week 4 – 5th November

Fasting, plus all the detoxing measures, felt pretty hard core. The next stage kicked in, which meant drinking a mixture of fresh pink grapefruit juice, mixed with olive oil. Yuk. Still marginally better than sauerkraut juice.

The grand finale of the cleanse was taking magnesium something-or-other. Something must have been working as I later passed about a gazillion small, luminous green stones! Sorry: that's probably a bit too much info! I was a bit pale and washed out; in a place full of cancer patients, everyone kept asking me whether I was okay. That's not good.

As the cleanse finished and we went back to eating properly, there was another little surprise for us. Wednesday was 'silence day'. Yes, absolute silence. Yet another first. Actually, I was quite looking forward to it. As I was feeling so tired, drained and delicate, it would be quite nice not to have to make conversation.

The rationale for the silence day was to provide time and space for you to listen to your intuition. This is what we were asked to consider:

Clarity and focus: what do you want?

Being happy: with yourself and your life.

Let go and forgive: yourself; other people?

Being grateful

We were encouraged to journal our thoughts, to read things that inspired us, to go out for a walk and to look for synchronicities.

These were hard questions to ask yourself, if you were thorough and honest. I worked on this throughout the day and enjoyed the silence.

We wrote letters to those we wished to forgive and got together later in the day to symbolically burn them - still in silence. I felt as though I was in a film, or part of a secret cult. It felt a million miles away from my former life. I liked it, though; it was a powerful and good experience.

I began to realise that I hadn't got much time left there, and much as I wanted to go home, I felt anxious about continuing on my own without any support.

Week 5 – 12th November

This was the last week of my training, before I went home and flew solo.

Things were not quite as I would have expected them to be at that stage. I felt worse than when I'd arrived, by a long chalk. .

What I mean by 'worse' is, I felt flu-ish; you know that feeling when everything hurts, even your eyelashes? I was exhausted. I felt like I was wearing a vice around my torso, which hurt when I breathed in, and hurt all the time on my left-hand-side ribcage. I also had electric-shock type pains in my right breast from time to time: I felt sore, and as though it might explode any minute, which wasn't good. Oh, and when I lay on my back, I felt as though an elephant was sitting on my sternum (breastbone to you non-medical types). I had a peep under the covers, and was pleased to know that an elephant wasn't actually there :-)

Reminds me of my favourite elephant joke ever:

How do you know if there's an elephant in your fridge? You can see footprints in the butter.

After four weeks at the Centre, it was not how I thought I would feel. I think the liver cleanse was the culprit - my goodness, it stirred up more than a few toxins! As well as expelling a gazillion little green stones, I felt much more emotional than normal; I had enough spots on my chin to qualify as a teenager, pains where I never knew I could have pains, and an almost hourly need for a nap. On the bright side, it showed that something was happening to my body. The phrase 'better out than in' sprang to mind. I had no appetite; it seemed to have got washed away with the little green stones.

Mr Darkfield-Analysis-Bloodman was pleased with my progress. All the cells were now single rather than clustered, as they should have been. The big crystals had broken down, meaning that I was more alkaline – which, again, was good.

On Thursday I had my meeting with Christa, one of the holistic therapists, to go through my treatment plan for home. I would be able to carry on with many of the lifestyle things I'd done there. Once we'd been through the details of my home plan, she mentioned the chap in Munich who did targeted chemo - the one the doctor had mentioned when I'd first arrived.

I asked her why she felt the need to mention this. She said that it was always good to have a Plan B, so that you could get on with treatment and on with your life, knowing that there was a Plan B if you needed it. I wondered if she felt the need to mention a Plan B to everyone, and thought that she probably didn't. Good to know, though. Information is good.

Reflecting on what I had learned and achieved in the five weeks at the 3E Centre, I found it easy to make a long list:

- Absolute confidence that this is the right route for me to follow, and that it will lead me to healing and wellness

- Full understanding of the 3E programme, so that I can take and transfer it into my life at home

- Changing my initial negative views of habit and routine, to being comforted by knowing what exactly I need to do every day to get well

- Confidence that I can make the programme work for me, even away from the safe haven of the 3E Centre

- A realisation of just how important my family and friends are to me; I literally couldn't have got through the experience alone without the support, messages, love and good wishes from everyone around me

- Had already made some improvements to my health (as proved in my blood results taken at the end, when compared with those taken at the beginning)

- The phrase "I'm going for a quick coffee" now means something completely different!

- I know the things I need to remove from my life so that I can protect my body from unnecessary stress

- I need to make the space and time for the things that give me most pleasure - this is my 'medicine', every bit as much as the food and detoxification

- I have learned that surviving without sugar, alcohol, processed foods, etc. is not only possible but also pleasurable, especially when you realise how happy it makes your body

- I am ready to share what I have learned with anyone who is interested, and people who are facing a similar situation - even if you have been pronounced "incurable"; there is hope and there is a way forward

- I have made some new friends; we have been there for each other during our stay

- I have learned that buckwheat is packed with vitamin B17 and that it's really good for you. I have also learned that I can't stand the stuff. Will continue the recipe search

- I now have a brilliant excuse to lie in the bath for 45 mins, as it now called detoxing and therapy, rather than indulgence and laziness

- Snuggling in bed with a hot water bottle is treatment for my liver which gives me a brilliant excuse for doing so.

Much as I was looking forward to going home, there was a twinge of sadness at leaving my buddies. Mrs Houston in particular - I couldn't have got through this without her. I felt so grateful to have been there. Although physically I didn't feel great, mentally I was in much better shape. I'd faced up to all sorts of demons and left no thoughts unturned.

I'd 'graduated'. Now the real work was to start.

How was I to do at home everything I'd been doing there - including shopping for, and preparing, organic vegetarian food; all the other 3E practices; and most importantly of all, keeping all the stresses of life to a minimum, at a time when I wouldn't have time to work, I'd have little money left and I would be undertaking the journey alone? The responsibility to cure myself of cancer weighed heavy.

I believed that I could do it but it felt like it would turn into a full-time job. What about my life? Would I have one outside juicing carrots?

Chapter 6 – Can an old dog learn new tricks? Woof!

I was home. Everything was pretty much as I'd left it. Yet everything was different. I was different.

I was so happy to be home. There's really nothing quite like it. The joy of sleeping in my own bed. The simple things in life really matter, don't they? I was really excited about my new life, wondering how I would be able to make it happen.

My other overriding feeling was anxiety. About whether I could manage to do everything I needed to do at a time when I was still suffering the after-effects of the liver cleanse; I had absolutely no energy and very little appetite.

The fact remained that I needed to get equipped for this new life. Where would I find the organic salad, fruit and vegetables I needed - the quark, flaxseed oil in glass bottles (not plastic) and the organic coffee for my enemas? Where would I have my enemas – I didn't have room for a bench in the bathroom like there was at the 3E Centre. I needed a rebounder but I wasn't sure one would fit in the car; could I order and have one delivered? I needed flax seeds to sprinkle over breakfast and a coffee grinder to smash them in. I needed to make vegetarian meals every day. I wondered how I could make them appetising. Where on earth did I get sauerkraut juice? Would I be able to find anything like my favourite fennel tea? When would I have the energy to go and look? I felt utterly overwhelmed with it all.

Everyone was really pleased that I was back – I spent lots of time on the phone, texting and answering messages, and a couple of people came round to say hello. I fished the juicer out from the back of the cupboard, and found that I'd forgotten how to use it. And forgotten where the instruction book was. It felt like the world was conspiring against me and my '3E-ness'. I wanted to get under the duvet and stay there.

The day passed in a blur and I couldn't get everything done in my schedule! That was not how it was supposed to be. Having said that, each day got a little bit easier as I caught up with my chores and ticked more things off my 'To Do List'.

Some of my blog posts from that time captured exactly how I was feeling:

Transition time – 20th November

Hello Team!

Sorry that I deserted you for a little while, hope I'm

forgiven. Most of Saturday was travelling and I spent Sat night, Sunday and Monday with my big sis and her gang. It was lovely to be spoiled, and to be surrounded by people I know, who make me laugh. She helped me work through my food shopping list, so that I have all the essentials food-wise. We also had some family time and it was great to join in Sunday lunch. Well, the veggie bit of it..

My sister had kept the Monday free so that we could spend some time together, just the two of us, which was lovely.

I did do bits of my routine while staying at theirs, but didn't have the kit and caboodle to do everything.

Then it was time to come back home, which I did yesterday evening (Monday). And that's when a whacking dose of reality hit.

A massive suitcase to unpack, with all that lovely washing and ironing. A huge pile of post to work through. A big food shop to put away, and various gadgets to dust off and get ready (the juicer and coffee grinder for the linseeds). Also, I'd had some essential decorating done while I was away, so there's a layer of dust over absolutely everything.

"So what?" you might say. "That's what happens when you come home from being away." Except that

it doesn't feel "so what". It feels pretty overwhelming.

There is only room in my head for the programme and what I should be doing at 7.15, 8.00, 10,00, etc. No space for all the other domestic stuff, and that's without even beginning to think about work!

It feels different than it did in Germany, where everything is laid out for you and you just turn up to collect it. And you are surrounded by people doing the same thing. Obviously, it's different - I knew that it would be. But what I maybe didn't expect is that I would feel a tad 'caught in the headlights', or that I'd wonder where I'd find the motivation and energy to do it all. I think I will have a look in the bottom of my handbag, that's where I often find what I'm looking for.

I have ticked a few things off the 'To Do List' today - not anywhere near as many as I wanted to, though. I haven't eaten enough and I didn't have a walk. The plan is to do more tomorrow and, if I get a bit more perfect each day, I should have my girly swot badge back by the end of the week. That's my aim.

Interestingly, one of the pieces of post that arrived whilst I was away in Germany was the appointment for me to attend the breast clinic for screening - you know, just in case there is a lump in my breast. Oh, the irony.

****

L Plates – 23rd November

I tried to figure out why I wasn't picking up where I'd left off in Germany, now that I was home.

Some of it was to do with my energy and motivation - I was still feeling a bit tired, and it's harder to motivate yourself when you're not surrounded by like-minded people..

I think the main factor was the newness. Do you remember what it's like when you start a new job, and everything takes you a lot longer to do? You don't know where to find the envelopes; you haven't yet established your routine, and you haven't figured out the best order to do things in. Well, that's how I felt. Let me give you a couple of examples:

One of the important parts of the 3E programme was the nutrition plan. Now that I was home, I had to shop for this and prepare it, whereas in Germany all I'd had to do was turn up and eat it. But I used to shop for food before I went, so why was this so different?

I used to just go to a supermarket and grab everything. Now, I had to be a lot more discerning; I had to look for organic goods, liquids need to be bottled in glass, not plastic – and, of course, there were

71

some specific foods that were really important on the Budwig diet. I found a really good quark in Asda and Waitrose. The flax oil I found in Sainsbury's. Buttermilk (which I can have on a morning as a replacement for sauerkraut juice) I could get in Tesco. Some of the other things I needed, such as flax seeds for the Linomel, organic cosmetics, etc., I could get from health food shops. All in all, shopping this week has taken me a lot longer than normal.

When it comes to cooking, I now prepare food on a very different basis than before. Totally vegetarian: no eggs, a bit of cheese allowed, no sugar, no processed foods, etc. And the pattern is: breakfast, a three-course lunch and a two-course light supper. Certainly very different than I've ever eaten before and there's some measure of effort in figuring out the menu each day. Again, it will get easier and easier.

The detox part of the 3E programme I found the easiest to fit in; I do it as part of my bedtime routine: the coffee enema, skin brushing and the bicarb of soda baths. Had an exciting breakthrough on the bicarb front! A tub from the supermarket - that would last me two baths - costs 99p; as it's something I need to do for the rest of my natural life, this could prove pretty costly. My genius niece, Lucie, decided to bulk buy, and had four-and-a-half stones of bicarb delivered to me which should keep me well looked after for a year or so, all for the princely sum of £38. Marvellous.

The other extremely important part of the plan is the mental work: visualising, affirmations, keeping stress at bay, relaxing, etc. It's all too easy for this to get squeezed out by the busyness of life and I need to guard against this. I do some visualising as I wake up, during my daily walk, and again, as part of my bedtime routine. Time with friends and having a giggle are also part of this; I'm gradually catching up with everyone now that I'm back, which is my favourite medicine of all.

I took the opportunity to visit The Haven this week - a charity supporting women with breast cancer. It's a really friendly place and I chose some therapies that will support me on the 3E programme. I had my first appointment this week for Shiatsu massage and it was fabulous. You lie on a mat on the floor; it's a very hands-on therapy that works to get your body and meridians back in balance. Next time we're going to work on my breathing, back, neck and shoulders. Can't wait.

Each day felt a bit easier. On my fourth day back in my own place I cut myself some slack. It took weeks for things to feel easy when I was in Germany, so if it took me a couple of weeks here that's not too bad, is it? My plan then was to make time for work - I craved and needed normality but the 3E programme HAS to come first.

Progress Report - 10th December

I had now been home for three full weeks. This meant that I'd been following the programme for eight weeks in total. Seemed like a good point to reflect..

First of all, where was I at mentally? I'd adapted pretty well to the programme, I thought. I'd been out to parties, eaten out and had visitors to me. In all of those circumstances I'd been just fine; the people around me have been really supportive.

No-one batted an eyelid when I had to say no to the canapés and the drinks - or if I needed something making especially for me, or if I brought my own. It was no big deal if my idea of having another drink involved putting the kettle on for a fruit infusion.

For those who came to see me, not only did they agree to just have what I was having (which was great - I didn't really want cupboards full of tempting things that I couldn't eat) they actually looked forward to trying new things, such as finding out what the infamous quark and oil tasted like. I think I've faced the trickiest situations, and it's all been just fine.

Where was I at physically? I was soooo glad that I'd kept a journal, so that I could look back and compare things with how I felt at that moment. Otherwise, it was all too easy to assume no progress had been made. Let's just compare how I was feeling *Before Germany* (B.G.) to how I felt after two short months on the programme:

B.G.

Right breast - extremely painful and tender to touch, couldn't even bear the seat belt across me. Intermittent shooting pains like an electric shock or stabbing with a needle. Breast very hard to the touch (where the tumour is, around the nipple and around the outside); nipple felt "dead". Across the top of the breast, a numb feeling as if I'd had a local anaesthetic.

Right armpit - swollen, the normal going-in shape had become a swollen coming-out egg shape; tender to touch

Sternum - extremely painful all the time. Very uncomfortable when lying down on my back; felt like an elephant was sitting on me - a big elephant, not some cute Dumbo-type.

Energy levels - low. Very rarely got through the day without needing a nap to recharge.

Now

Right breast - nowhere near as painful; no problem with seatbelt. Not hard on the inside of the breast near the nipple. Some sensation in the nipple. Very occasional sharp pain. A sensation of itching all over from time to time. A feeling of numbness but less so, and only near the sternum.

Right armpit - goes in, in an armpit-like fashion. Not painful, although if I squeezed my arm into my body, there was a "bruised" sensation, and also the same on my left armpit. Felt a lump in my left armpit if I did a touch examination.

Sternum - a little bit sore if I pressed to examine it. Even on close examination I cannot find an elephant - not even a teeny tiny one. Some loss of sensation towards the right breast. Able to lay on my front, albeit briefly.

Energy levels - much better. I didn't need a little nap to get through the day. I went for walks that lasted over an hour without any problem. I looked better too - I had this on the good authority of my sister, who can be honest with me as no-one else can.

She told me that she expected I'd look quite well-rested on my return from Germany (I should have done, with the amount of sleep I had!) but that I actually looked quite poorly. This was news to me, because I'd thought I looked pretty good! She confirmed that I didn't anymore... phew! I really did not want to look ill, and I was therefore delighted when people told me how well I looked.

The verdict?

I think that we can agree that this was pretty good. In just eight weeks there were lots of good indicators. I say this with a note of caution, while crossing my fingers and touching numerous wooden objects - I don't want to count any chickens, and feel nervous of being too cocky too soon.

There are some things that are new symptoms (like the lump under my left armpit and a couple of other things) which I need to keep a watchful eye over. But it is easy to be a tad paranoid and think that everything is to do with cancer when, in actual fact, we all have aches, pains and niggles from time to time, don't we? Obviously, in my circumstance, they could feel more significant.

The programme was now my new way of life: it was getting easier as time went on. I had the support of you guys standing right alongside me, cheering me on. I was starting to see results that made it all worthwhile, and which increased my already unshakeable belief that this was the right course of action for me.

One of Those Days - 17th December

We all have them, don't we? Mine started as soon as I woke up - I could feel swelling in my right armpit. My breast felt really uncomfortable and now I even had a lump in my left armpit. For two pins, I could have gone back to bed with the duvet over my head. But no... come on, Nina....

Feeling physically unwell is no fun - my heart goes out to those people who are really in pain, perhaps constantly. I find that it puts a dampener on my mood and my face forgets it can smile. Playing on my mind was a text I'd got a couple of days before, from a friend who "sees things"; a spiritual type - I'd previously opened myself up to the possibilities of healing and the spiritual world. The text told me, in a roundabout way, that they thought I was going to die - not in so many words but that was what the text meant. Just what I needed to read. Not.

In this state of mind, it is far too easy to notice the not-so -good things, isn't it? I followed my usual routine: the *Swish and Go*, the buttermilk, the tablets, breakfast, making fresh juice, three course lunch, etc. I found myself thinking, 'Is this it? Every day for the rest of my life I will be doing this, loading the juicer into the dishwasher, making a shopping list of the things I can see I'm running out of - is this it? I feel like a hamster on a treadmill.'

Time to stop feeling sorry for myself, I resolved, so I vowed to do absolutely every single thing on my schedule, and really throw myself into it. That would hopefully shake off the physical symptoms within a few days. So I did. I always feel better in action mode. All was going well until a phone call later in the day. It was one where I needed to discuss my medical situation. I had never spoken to the person on the other end of the phone before. They referred to me as "someone with an advanced stage of cancer"; this may sound strange given my diagnosis but this is not how I think of myself, and I certainly don't like to hear that description. There were some other things: a disappointment about something I was looking forward to. But enough wallowing!

It's interesting how the little things we can deal with seem to get huge when they stack up one after the other. Also, when in this spiral, it is all too easy to focus on what's going wrong, to the exclusion of the other things which are not. Which is why I decided to blog: to give more attention to the good things.

The tally of things that had gone right was actually pretty high: a great meeting, banter with my business partner, delicious food, the satisfaction of following the programme 100%, a couple of phone calls from friends asking how I was, firming up arrangements to catch up with two friends who I hadn't seen for far too long (yes, Sally - one of them was YOU!); an invitation to be February's inspirational WOW Woman on a well-read blog, someone saying 'you've lost weight', and a possible first-date on Saturday. Not too shabby for 'one of those days', was it?

Note to self - do not dwell on the not-so-good things, look for and focus on the good.

Treading on eggshells? 23rd December

It can be difficult - what do you say to someone in my situation? Do you say 'how are you?' and risk being told everything in spectacularly graphic medical detail? Or worse still, get a shouted, 'how do you think I am? I've got CANCER!'"

I don't think that there is one stock answer on what to say. I usually take my cue from the person I am talking to. Some people have an immense amount of curiosity about the medical stuff, and that's fine by me. Others are more interested in how I am and life in general, and that's fine too. Others just make me laugh, which is brilliant.

The only reaction I had which I found really strange and difficult to cope with was someone who would not even acknowledge that anything was happening, so we had to 'skirt' round things. Now that was awkward - so I wouldn't recommend that.

In essence, I would say that all of us just have to be ourselves. In spite of my diagnosis, I didn't change into a different person overnight. I was still as silly, although I guess I had more serious moments, but that's all they were: moments.

And you should still be you; if discussing business is the norm, then carry on. If sharing updates on each other's lives is the usual, then do that. Friends commented that things in their life seemed trivial in comparison, and they were therefore reluctant to raise them. Just remember, to your friends, your 'stuff' is never trivial, because they care about you. And there HAS to be more than cancer to talk about. Life goes on...

If there is someone in your life who is going through big 'stuff', I would say to you:

- DO reach out

- DO offer to lend a hand with something practical, or do something thoughtful to make them smile

- DON'T always wait to be asked. It is hard to ask for help, and sometimes the unbidden kindnesses and surprises mean so much more. When I was in Germany, I would never have thought to ask for a cat mask for Halloween, a David Beckham cushion, or a Blue Peter-type 'make something colourful' kit, but they sure cheered me up

- In short, be the friend you have always been

I would like to share a note that I received on Facebook, from someone I didn't actually know that well. Once you read it, I am sure you will be able to imagine the impact it had on me. It uplifted me, made me feel confident and about ten feet tall; I re-read it whenever I need a boost.

I just wanted to let you know that I was upset to hear your news.

Then I thought about it.

Then it dawned on me that, from the little I actually got to know of you during our brief career intersection, there was nothing to be sad about.

Because you're an inspiration. You're a tour de force. You're one of those people who 'does'.

Nancy Sinatra said, 'these boots are made for walking' and I'm sure that your shoes (every pair rivalling Imelda Marcos') will trample over and kick seven bells out of this challenge.

We're all with you, every step. Go get 'em, tiger xxx

98 Days Later – 19th January 2013

I had been following the 3E programme for 98 days. Or, 14 weeks. Or, what seems like a lifetime. Time to review progress. It seemed a long time since I'd felt "normal". Okay, so I've never been that normal, but you know what I mean..

I felt a bit outside of 'normal' life - I looked on while people ordered a glass of wine and said "cheers". I declined when friends were going out to eat late (which, for me, is post-6pm) as that wasn't part of my new regime. I glanced at my watch periodically, not consciously, but with constant thoughts of what needs doing next so that I will have ticked all the things on my list at the end of each day. It was not yet so hard-wired that I got it all done without conscious thought.

I have to say that sticking to the Budwig diet didn't really bother me. I changed my attitude towards food. Instead of thinking "ooh, what would I like to eat?" I considered food as important as medicine and nutrients, and assessed what my body needed. It helped that I had a fondness for lots of healthy foods such as beetroot, mushrooms, spinach and chickpeas (the love affair I had with Lamb Henry, bacon sandwiches and a cheeky little sauvignon blanc was firmly in the past and I had to move on).

Keeping stress-free was a bit of a

challenge. Life tended to get in the way of that. The financial pressures of this alternative path I'd chosen fell on me. The NHS were saving a fortune from me not having chemo and all that malarkey, but that didn't mean they would chip in for the Germany trip or my rather hefty organic carrot bill. Shame.

My biggest stress continued to be fitting everything into a day. I needed my sleep (always have, so don't see that changing any time soon). I don't remember sitting around twiddling my thumbs BG (before Germany), as running a business, a home, a social life, and spending time with family and friends filled my days. Now that I had to fit in all of that, plus the whole 3E programme's daily regime (which took approximately three to five hours a day), I continually wished that I had more hours in the day. I either needed a team of domestic staff, or to get more organised and focused and sleep less. As someone who has never ever been a creature of habit, the other challenging aspect was doing the same things day in, day out. It felt a tad like 'Groundhog Day'.

I hope I don't sound like I'm complaining, because I'm absolutely not. I just want to tell it like it is: this was how it felt. I was still very, very happy with my choice. This was the right route for me and I had absolutely no doubt of that, no matter what.

I had wondered if I'd taken the easy option. The brave people were the ones facing the chemotherapy, the surgery and the radiotherapy. I take my hat off to anyone going through that treatment, and send my best wishes for your recovery and wellness. I came to the conclusion, though, that mine wasn't an easy option, just a different option. It took a certain amount of discipline and focus to follow this, day in, day out. And I will need to do this for a number of years, maybe even for the rest of my life.

The other aspect which made me believe that it wasn't an easy option is that there wasn't a support infrastructure around me. The doctors didn't know or understand what I was doing. The support groups offered lots of things which the bulk of cancer patients need: help with the side-effects of the treatment. If I needed a wig, or alternative therapies to alleviate nausea or sleeplessness, then I would be well looked after. But I didn't.

When I was originally going for chemo, my friends and family were ready to spring into action. They knew that it could be physically really hard, so I had volunteers for cleaning, ironing, chauffeur duty, and company on treatment days. Because I had gone unilateral, none of us knew what to expect. Help was there if I asked for it, but I didn't know what to ask for. For the route I'd chosen, I was the only expert I had access to. Which was pretty scary, considering it was new to me too. I didn't feel like an expert.

And finally, the question that everyone asked me. How did I know that it was working? The honest answer is that I didn't. What I knew was the physical symptoms I was feeling. The tumour in my breast continued to grow, and I could feel it near the surface. I had feelings of numbness and tenderness under my arm, back and towards my shoulder blade. I had a hard lump in my right armpit that was tender right down my arm to the bend of my elbow. It was really disappointing. I didn't expect overnight miracles, but I did hope that it all might have a bit of a snooze whilst I was getting on with boosting my immune system.

It was still early days, though. When starting a new job, I always used to do myself a 100-day plan, to make sure I made a difference in the first three months, and that time used to whizz by.

The plan now was to keep the faith. To carry on with the programme and make even more effort to do every single thing I could, every single day. I was due blood tests soon. My liver knew that I expected it to be a high achiever and I promised it a double-espresso enema if it did well.

Team Nina visualised me healthy, well and all mended. Their love and good wishes were magic.

****

When I look back, I see so clearly what was going on for me, and what I was trying, perhaps a bit too subtly to communicate through my blog.

I really wished that someone would come along and take over. To do some of the practical things and tell me to sit down and concentrate on getting well.

I felt that I didn't fit in anywhere – not with the 'normal' people, who can eat out at 9pm, take their health for granted and therefore have the energy to do other things. Nor did I fit in with the cancer patients who needed help with wigs, nausea and the side effects of drugs. I officially didn't belong anywhere. It's a lonely business, being a maverick.

The fact that I looked okay confused the issue. Like many other unseen conditions, I guess. Because I wasn't bald or wearing a plaster cast, or walking with a white stick, it was easy for everyone to forget. Except me. Everyone said, 'ask if you need anything'. Do you have any idea how hard that is to do? Even thinking about it makes me squirm. When you are used to being strong and independent, to ask for help feels like weakness, an admission of being ill. And I couldn't go there, could I?

I wished that I understood the impact all this was having on other people around me. The friends who I didn't hear from at all. The friends who distanced themselves, so I didn't see them anywhere near as much as I did B.G. Did they think that cancer was catching? Or that it reminded them of their own mortality? Or that they were scared of losing me, so if we saw each other less now it made the loss easier. For them. Or maybe I was just plain boring now that I had cancer. The friends who kept saying, 'let's go out soon'; *soon never came.* Or, best of all, 'let's go out when you're better'. Jeez, the things a girl has to do to get a night out! Just cure yourself of cancer, that's all.

I genuinely didn't understand why they thought it was okay to leave things so long for someone with an apparently limited life expectancy. What if they didn't get round to it before it was too late? That would be a shame, wouldn't it? I did appreciate that everyone was busy and that they had their own lives but sometimes, things have to move up the priority list. Like me.

This cancer thing is pretty difficult to navigate. What I do know is that everyone does their best.

Let me make something very clear, though. No matter how challenging it all seemed, I was still absolutely happy with my choice. It was definitely the right course of action for me. My healthy cells and liver were having an absolute ball. Even if the cancer didn't appear to be shrinking.

I had cast iron resolve to continue with what I was doing, and the trust that it would lead me to where I needed to be. I was determined to be the best 3E graduate girly swot ever.

Chapter 7 – And they all lived happily ever after. Right?

This is where I tell you about how I was miraculously cured. That's what happens in the other books. Like Anita Moorjani in 'Dying To Be Me'. And Brandon Bays in 'The Journey'. I read lots of these books. The Haven had shelves of them, and I love to read. I devoured every page. I needed to bolster my belief that cancer could be successfully tackled by doing things differently. In some ways, they did help. But in others, not so much. I just felt a bit of a failure. Why couldn't I do what they did? I was doing everything I possibly could and still my cancer wasn't halting, never mind miraculously disappearing.

I faced some difficult realities, especially on the financial front. Following a programme like this was a full time job so I didn't have the time (or energy, for that matter) to work and, as I was self-employed, I was therefore not earning a bean. And I was supposed to be minimising stress in my life! In order to access money in my pension, I had to deal with the company I used to work for. That in itself was incredibly stressful. I wouldn't wish that process on anyone, especially not someone who's ill and where time is of the essence. Eventually, after much to-ing and fro-ing, I found out that I needed to have a letter stating that my life expectancy was less than 12 months I therefore had to have this discussion with my doctor.

I had never had this discussion before. I didn't really want to have it at all. Once you've heard an expert tell you that you only have 'x' amount of months to live, you can't *un-know* that information.

Apparently, my doctor could provide the data to the insurance company that they needed, and prove that my life expectancy was less than 12 months. So that was good news: I would be able to access funds to alleviate the financial pressure. But clearly it was not great news, as I now had to deal with knowing that piece of information and still remain positive.   In this interaction with my doctor, we had to acknowledge how much the disease had progressed. At the time, I didn't share this in my blog as it felt too personal, even for me who was sharing everything. I didn't want to send everyone running for the hills or to have them feel sorry for me.

Here is the entry I made in my private journal:

Sunday 10*th* February

A bit of a week. Probably the worst one so far. It started on Monday at Jimmy's, seeing the Prof. She will confirm that my life expectancy is less than 12 months, which will resolve the £ situation I hope. She also talked about some other things which were hard to listen to. If the tumour breaks through the skin, as it seems about to do, then an op won't work, but radiotherapy might help. I feel like a leper as it's so unsightly. She seems to think there's a problem with my lungs. I have been a bit short of breath. She says I may get fluid on my lungs which could be drained. She found a lump in my neck. Felt really dark this week. I am so uncomfortable; it's painful and I don't have much energy or motivation for anything. I wish I had someone here with me to chivvy me along and do some of it with or for me. I feel really isolated and don't know who or where to turn.

Will be nice to get the money thing sorted – I will have some more Vit C, I think. Would love to go away somewhere warm more than anything, but don't know if I dare, or if I'm up to it. Think I'm just having a bad week. Hopefully things will look better soon. For the first time this week, I thought 'this isn't working', and that I can't last long. Not if it continues growing at this rate. That this might be my last birthday. Need to get into action mode to move out of this gloom.

13th February

I have had two days when I've stayed in my PJs all day and slept a lot. It was the snow's fault today. Although I have done some things. However, time to stage a comeback. The pain hasn't been anywhere near as bad the last couple of days (uncomfortable, though). The Salvestrol cream arrived today, so I will slap some of that on. I have to be up tomorrow to go to Shiatsu, so that will do me good. Think I will put my glam on. Time to remind myself of everything I'm grateful for: I will do that when I've finished this rambling. My life expectancy letter arrived from the hospital today, so I can get moving with that. That will be a major milestone, can't wait. It will make every other single thing easier.

Interestingly, that was the last entry I made in my handwritten journal. You may wonder why. I guess I got busy. Let me explain:

Despite how I was feeling physically, mentally, I was feeling pretty strong. I needed something to focus on, something to achieve that would help me look towards the future. I didn't know exactly what, but then, as often happens in life, an opportunity presented itself.

My friend and well-known speaker, Richard McCann, was planning to hold a speakers' event and he asked me if I would like to speak. I didn't hesitate and said yes immediately. It was just what I needed. I was getting great feedback on my blog; it was proving to be entertaining and informative to people, and with my background I thought that speaking about my experiences was a natural extension to that.

The event was planned for 22nd February. I prepared for it in-between my other activities, whenever I felt I had the energy. I rested lots in the run-up to the event as it was going to be a full day. Although I had spoken to big and small groups many times, this would be the first time I'd talked about something so personal: something I was still going through, where I didn't know how the story would eventually unfold.

On the day, many of my friends and Team Nina members were in the audience to support me, which was great. I shared my story with the audience, telling them how and why I had decided to do what I did. It felt good and the feedback and comments I got afterwards convinced me even more that I should speak out and share what I was learning. It felt good to have a project to focus on.

Here are some of my blog entries from the time which explain how I felt about this:

I Can, Can I?

27th February

In the couple of weeks prior to the 'I Can' event I have to admit that it did cross my mind "why on earth did I agree to do this?" Which is most unlike me, when given the opportunity to speak to a captive audience! I have been speaking to groups for many, many years, and love to do so. So, why was I feeling like this?.

A diagnosis like mine is a life-changing event, and my confidence is not as shiny and strong as it once was. Also, I have had a break from speaking as I have been a little busy with other priorities over the last few months, as you know. And the content of my speech, not only is it extremely personal, it's recent; in fact, I am still going through it, with new (and not always positive) things happening all the time. All good reasons to be feeling as I did, I think?

But that was not the main factor, actually. The main reason was the hospital appointment I had on the 4th Feb, which I have told you about. After hearing everything that's likely to happen next, and the treatment I would need, I felt really, really low. And very alone. The worst I have felt since all of this started. To say that I was not in the frame of mind to prepare a motivational speech is an understatement. I guess I was not, therefore, as prepared as I would have normally liked.

However, because I had a deadline to work to and had to prepare, despite all this, I had to get on with it. And it proved to be just what I needed. Having to articulate all the reasons I decided to do what I'm doing reconnected me with everything positive about my course of action. Marvellous.

In the few days before the event, my biggest issue was … you guessed it … what to wear. As the event branding was black and gold, I decided to take this as my cue, and the gold sequins therefore were a must. On the Friday night, my talented hairdresser sister, Julie, came to do my hair, so that it would be easy for me just to titivate on Saturday morning.

On the morning of the event I felt nervous as I was getting ready. But when I got to the venue it all started to fall into place. My niece, Lucie, and brother-in-law, David, were with me which was like wearing a warm, safe security blanket. (My sister was at work. I had asked her not to come; if I had seen her whilst telling my story, I think I would have not been able to hold back the tears, and I didn't want to risk a mascara malfunction).

Richard (McCann), who was hosting the event, was brilliant as always, checking I was okay. I enjoyed the camaraderie with the other speakers, especially Kimm who, as a friend and healer, was helping me along this journey. And, of course, there were lots of Team Nina in the room. I felt like it was my party and all my chums had come. Not all of T.N. could make it, but I got lots of lovely messages and wishes, so you were with me in spirit.

When it was my turn, I really enjoyed sharing my story. It felt like absolutely the right thing to do. The audience seemed genuinely interested to hear it and the time just flew by. My message, although sad in parts, is ultimately positive and uplifting, and I am proud to say that I got more laughs than tears; no mean feat given the subject matter!

When I got back to my table, I got a "see, I knew you could do it" look from Lucie, and David leaned over to squeeze my hand. So, I knew I'd done good. At lunchtime and in the breaks, many people came to speak to me. To thank me for sharing my message, to tell me a bit about their story, and to ask questions. This, along with comments on Twitter and on this blog, help me to see that sharing all this really does strike a chord and connects me with people who want or need to know more.

It was a fabulous day. A really special experience for all concerned, and I am proud and happy to have been a part of it. Thank you, Richard, for asking me.

I will be getting some video clips and photos, so I will share these with you. I would definitely like to do more in future - so if you know anyone who books speakers, who would like to be inspired, entertained and be dazzled (the sequins can come out again) whilst hearing some messages that really matter, please point them my way. After all, I now know I can keep it together, and I need to be able to invite my sister to come and see me next time.

****

Physically, the story was not as positive. At the fateful life-expectancy appointment with the doctor, she had asked me if she could request a Macmillan nurse to visit me, as I may be entitled to some other financial help. I reluctantly and, no doubt, grumpily agreed.

I didn't like the idea at all, of needing a Macmillan nurse, or of needing financial help. When the Macmillan nurse came to see me, she also filled in an application form for a disabled badge for the car which, given that I was having difficulty breathing and walking, might be helpful. But I didn't like that idea either. She then moved the conversation to palliative care. By the time she left, although it had been practical and helpful, my spirits were through the floor. I had never felt more like a cancer patient.

Reality Check   9th March

I had an interesting conversation with a very perceptive friend of mine. He was telling me about how he feels when reading my blog. He referred in particular to one of my more recent posts; 'The Good News, and the Not So Good News'. He felt that I had stopped myself from saying more, from saying what needed saying. I think he is absolutely right. I reflected on this, wondering why I "censored" myself. I think I was trying to protect you from the truth, which is a bit patronising really, isn't it? And defeats the object of the blog. Sorry. I intend to put that right, and tell it as it really is. Without any positive spin. It is now over six months since I was diagnosed with cancer. A lot has happened in this time, especially to my body. Let's take a full reality check on what that means and how it impacts on me..

The tumour in my breast was large when it was found, and it's still growing. I know it is because I can feel it and can see it, and new symptoms seem to appear every morning just to remind me. Some days the skin is incredibly sensitive, even the stitching inside clothing feels like pins sticking into me. I sometimes have sharp pains, like an electric shock, which takes my breath away. The area around my breastbone/sternum is tender and painful.

I now have a tumour in my right armpit - it is hard and really uncomfortable. It means that around my armpit and upper arm I have some numbness, which is strange. I have pain and restricted movement in my right arm - this is due to hardened lymph vessels, called 'cording'. It makes it difficult for me to do some things: reaching the top kitchen cupboards, closing the car boot, changing the bed (it's difficult changing a double bed on your own anyway, if you ask me), holding the lid open on the big wheelie rubbish bins and being strong enough to lift the rubbish with my other arm, to mention a few.

I have some fluid on my lung. This means I feel short of breath for no apparent reason. Also, when I lay down to sleep, I can hear it when I breathe - it's like hearing someone blow through a straw into liquid. Which brings back really poignant memories of the chest infection Mum had; of sitting at her hospital bed, holding her hand and hearing her laboured breathing right until she died.

Thankfully, I am not aware of any symptoms from the tumour in my liver.

I now have a small tumour at the base of my throat. No symptoms from this either.

If I do too much, I can feel incredibly tired. Abnormally so. For example, after a busy day last week, I realised that I had run out of buttermilk, so I had to make a trip to Tesco. When I parked the car, I felt utterly exhausted, and had to have a power nap for 10 mins before I could face going into the store.

Reality check time. For someone who has been following a very strict regime for the last 5 months, this is not what I imagined would be my reality at this point. I am supposed to be curing myself. Surely it should be at least halted, if not improved?

Time is not on my side, remember? Of the women

diagnosed with my type and stage of cancer, half of them die within 4 months! So, much as I would like to chill out and give time for my regime to get my body back in kilter, I am nervous about waiting to see what I can achieve over time. But who can I ask? Because I've gone all unilateral about my chosen treatment, the expert in all of this is me!!! Me, who knew absolutely zip about cancer until August last year, has no medical knowledge, and who has a really big problem with attention to detail.

I realised just how isolated I felt when I caught the new Macmillan advert on television. It's about how no-one should face cancer alone. That's not how it feels. It made me cry.

So, what to do? Feel depressed? Give up?

Hell, no.

*But it **is** time to reconsider my tactics. Consult my intuition and my gut instinct, like I did when I decided to go to the 3E Centre. Recruit some new expert members to Team Nina, perhaps?*

And above all, to get together my very cunning plan on what to do next. So cunning you could pin a tail on it and call it a fox. Except, I like a bit of glamour, as you know, so I'm going to call it 'Foxy' instead.

Plan Foxy will be an absolute corker. More details

soon. Keep sending me your positive vibes, or praying, or whatever your thang is. Thank you x

****

My birthday was on 16th March and I remember how I felt. I was in considerable pain. I was having difficulty breathing as I had fluid on my lungs, which meant that I had to walk quite slowly and deliberately. I went into Leeds to meet my friends Rita and Sue, as we had planned to go on the Leeds Eye. My niece, Lucie, came to pick me up and escort me, otherwise I don't think I could have made it. We stopped for a drink and something to eat, as you do on your birthday, but I couldn't face anything so just had a smoothie. I genuinely felt that it may have been my last birthday, although I didn't say that out loud.

Was this it? The beginning of the end? I thought not, but I didn't know what to do about it.

Alongside being busy preparing for the 'I Can' event, I'd been considering what to do. I didn't like the two options in front of me. Option one: carry on with just the 3E programme. Although I felt this was good for my healthy cells, clearly the situation with the cancer was deteriorating. My cancer was just too advanced. Option two: ask for the conventional chemo treatment that was originally offered. But I didn't believe that was right then, and actually, I still didn't now. What could I do? Where could I do?

In my financial background, we had what are called 'Tied Agents': those who are trained and knowledgeable about the products of just one company, the company they are employed by. We also had IFAs - Independent Financial Advisers - people who would scan the whole of the market and advise you on the product that was best for you. Why am I telling you this? I saw doctors as Tied Agents: expert and knowledgeable, but only on the things they had been trained on (chemo, radiotherapy, surgery). I badly wanted to talk to a cancer IFA, but there didn't seem to be such a thing. Or if there was, I didn't know how to find them.

Luckily, the answer to that landed in my lap. Well, through my post box, to be precise. A friend of mine had relayed a bit of my story at one of the Professional Speaking Association meetings I hadn't been able to attend while I was at the 3E Centre. A lady in the audience offered to send some information that could have proved useful to me, and my friend passed it on. As I was feeling so overwhelmed at the time and because I had been so busy with my regime, the information had stayed in my folder, untouched.

But now, as I was looking for other options, I paid attention. Amongst the magazine articles there was a leaflet for an organisation called *Yes to Life* - a charitable initiative aiming to offer choices and information to people with cancer looking for an integrative approach to cancer care. My antennae started twitching immediately. I went on the website to see what I could see. And that's where I found her: Patricia Peat of Cancer Options, offering 'a unique and unbiased appraisal of both orthodox and complementary approaches'. My cancer IFA!

I felt excited; I somehow knew this was it, what I'd been looking for. My blog tells the story of what happened at this crucial point in my story, and how it unfolded:

Plan Foxy coming together – 19th March

Right then, I've got my mind back in a more positive place. But there's no denying that the physical symptoms are there and getting more noticeable, to me, anyway. I am pretty good at covering up so that others don't notice..

Listening to my body, to my gut instinct, I know that something else needs to happen. The 3E programme has kept me well for longer than anyone would have expected. I feel that it has got my healthy cells in tip-top condition and looked after my immune system, liver and digestive system, so that I am in pretty good shape. Considering.

It hasn't, however, brought the tumours to a halt. I know this from the ones I can feel - in my breast and in my lymph glands. And because I have a new tumour in my neck. And fluid on my lungs and shortness of breath. This is not the plan! I'm not going to just sit around and let that happen now, am I?

I now know that I need to do more to zap the cancer cells, and therefore decide to consult an expert. Not a doctor, not a holistic therapist. But someone who knows about it all, the whole spectrum: from conventional to the most unconventional. As you know, my professional background is in financial services, and I wanted the equivalent of an Independent Financial Adviser in the medical world. Someone who could advise on 'whole of market', with no particular bias. Who could speak from experience and say what they know, what they have seen and what they believe will work for me - ideally alongside my current regime, as it has looked after me so far, and is incredibly good for my body.

As often happens in life, once you start knocking on a few doors the universe conspires to help you. An absolute stranger heard about what I was doing through a friend of mine and took the time and trouble to send me some leaflets and information she thought may be of use to me. (Thank you, Rebecca).

Amongst this information was a leaflet on a charity called Yes to Life - see www.yestolife.org.uk. They are committed to opening up a positive future for people with cancer in the UK by supporting an integrative approach to cancer care. As you can imagine,

I scoured their website looking at the information and resources available. I felt like I had found a little haven where there were people like me, people who understood me. Many things were useful, but perhaps the most significant was finding Patricia Peat of Cancer Options (www.canceroptions.co.uk) - my IFA! She has a background in orthodox medicine but is now a fountain of knowledge on all available approaches.

I arranged to see her - to tell her about my situation and to find out what she could offer. After about ten minutes, I decided that she is very definitely a new expert member of Team Nina.

She has many thoughts on how I can up the ante on attacking the cancer alongside my 3E programme. This will include vitamin C and oxygen therapy, plus many more if we need them (more about that later). But significantly, she also thought that I could benefit from a technique used very successfully in Germany called TACE. This had been mentioned to me by the doctor and holistic therapist at the 3E Centre. Because the cancer has spread and is so advanced, it was their view that I should have a back-up plan, and Patricia too was of the opinion that it would help me. When you hear something more than once, from sources that you trust, it is time to listen.

TACE stands for (here comes the science bit) trans-arterial chemo-embolisation. Or, to put it into Nina speak; targeted chemotherapy, injected directly into the tumour. Because the whole body is not subjected to the chemotherapy, a concentration many, many times stronger can be used. And because it doesn't get to the rest of your body, the side effects are minimal. I am liking the sound of this. A lot.

So, to cut a long story short, I have been accepted for treatment by Professor Vogl who is internationally renowned for his work in this field. I fly to Frankfurt tomorrow, accompanied by my sister, Julie, to have the first treatment on Thursday before flying home on Friday. I feel incredibly lucky that I have found these people to help me that they are willing to work with me, and that it is all about to happen.

When I come home, I will be pulling together Plan Foxy; my mind is in shape, the cancer will have had a bit of a zapping, and I need to get on with looking after myself, living my life and making exciting plans to look forward to. Wish me luck!

TACE, the patient's experience – 24th March

The day dawned. Time to pop over to Frankfurt for the "'minimally invasive, maximally effective" TACE chemotherapy..

We reported to the hospital for 8 a.m., registered, and paid for the treatment. First, we met with the Prof, to talk through the plan for treatment and the plan for the day. He was calm, efficient and professional, exactly as you would expect. I liked him.

The first phase would be all about getting the large tumour in my breast and lymph under control, as that is what is causing me the most pain and discomfort. The plan for the day started with an MRI scan - my first scans since being diagnosed last September. I was really worried about this, in that on realising just how much the tumour had grown, he might not be prepared to treat me. Luckily, no such thing happened, but I certainly hadn't taken it for granted.

I was taken through to theatre and prepped. All the pics from the MRI scan were displayed above my head for the Prof to use. Fascinating! It was to be done under local anaesthetic, so I couldn't feel my right leg from the knee upwards and was aware of everything going on. I had a drip in with painkillers, etc. I was all covered up other than by my groin, where the incision was made. Ouch! Then the catheter was inserted, a strange sensation to say the least. Some dye was inserted which I could see on the screen above me. Once they could see it was all going to the right place, the Prof came and administered the chemo. It didn't take long at all. I had to keep my right leg totally straight and had a drip in my right arm. I was taken to a day ward for three hours where I was kept under observation to make sure all was okay.

I was then able to get dressed and was

taken back downstairs for a CT scan, to check that everything was as it should have been. At this point I was reunited with my sister, who was in the Prof's waiting room. This was probably about three-ish, from memory. The only thing to be done before leaving was to meet once more with the Prof to review what had happened and agree on what happened next.

His clinic was extremely busy. It was actually about 6.30 p.m. before we were seen. A long, long day. But it was all worth it. He did say that he couldn't work miracles, and that the tumour was extremely large - which I knew, after all, I'd been wearing it! He expected good results, although it would take several treatments, perhaps four or five. When I asked about my lungs and liver, he said that this would be Phase 2. Looks like I'd be making many more Frankfurt trips over the coming months. I asked him what I could do to aid the treatment; he said that I should live a long and happy life, as I was now on his statistics. I liked that answer. I wanted him to care that I looked good on his results!

Although tired, we strolled back to our hotel absolutely elated. That he **could** treat me, that he **would** treat me, and that we had started on the next phase of the journey. I could feel the tension releasing from my neck and shoulders and slept better than I had done for a while.

Tumour Watch – 1st April

It is now eleven days since my treatment. Most of that time has been spent with my duvet. We're very close. I think it's love. I cannot believe how long and how deeply I can sleep! It's a shame that it's not an Olympic event; I would be the golden girl, not Jessica..

But I guess my body is pretty busy. And that can take it out of a girl, ya know? It's obviously early days, but I thought I would share with you what's happening.

The whacking lumpy, horrible tumour in my right armpit, which means I can't lay on my right side, and that I don't quite know where to put my arm when I'm lying on my left - the one which means I have areas of numbness in that area, and "cording" which restricts me moving my arm - is very definitely less prominent. I have even found myself on my right side on occasions during my many, many hours in bed. The cording which I could feel on the inside of my elbow has now completely gone. And this after treatment one of four or five. I am feeling cautiously, optimistically ecstatic.

The fluid I had in my lung, I dare hardly say, seems to have cleared. I can breathe better, I don't cough all the time, and am not quite as out of breath when walking. Which is all the more impressive when you consider that I haven't even had any treatment on my lungs!

111

What I do know is that my mind and spirit and optimism are exactly where they need to be. And we all know that is bound to make me feel better physically. On my birthday, I found myself seriously wondering if it would be the last one I would celebrate... I don't feel like that now.

Some people have asked me if I wish I had had chemo earlier. My answer to that is an absolute, unequivocal no. There I go, sitting on that fence again. If I had acted in haste, as our medical system actively encourages, then I would have blindly followed the conventional route, even though every bone in my body told me it was the wrong thing, and even though the doctors knew it wouldn't cure me.

With the luxury of the time given me by following the 3E programme, I have been able to stay well longer than anyone in the know seems to think I should have or could have. This has enabled me to research and to increase my knowledge on what's available, and listen to and learn what is happening to my body.

In case I doubted my course of action, a friend of mine shared this story with me recently; he has another friend of similar age to me who was also diagnosed with advanced metastatic breast cancer last summer. She had chemotherapy, but this was very hard on her body. She sadly died on 14th February, weighing under 4 stones. Thank you for sharing this with me, Simon. I know it has been very difficult for you.

I am very, very lucky, and I know that. The route I am taking is not one that would suit everyone; it's challenging, it's sometimes lonely and it's bloody expensive! But it's the one that has my name written all over it, and the one I'm destined to take. Exciting, huh?

Tic Tacs – A.K.A Tactics - 23rd April

Hello Team, how are you all? Time for an update, there are developments to report..

Everything I have been doing so far has kept me relatively well. I feel as though my healthy cells are being looked after, but let's not kid ourselves that the cancer cells have been affected. They haven't, they are still growing. I know that from the tumours I can feel (breast and lymph;, I have some symptoms of breathlessness which must be something to do with the tumour in my lung, and the appearance of the newest addition to the tumour line-up in my neck tells us something, doesn't it? None of it good. And that's without even thinking about liver and bones.

So, this is why I decided to go to Frankfurt to get the targeted chemo. The first treatment has definitely had impact: the tumour under my arm is definitely smaller and causing me less discomfort. I think it has made a difference to the breast tumour too, but less so. I have very high hopes for this treatment, but the main downside is that only one tumour can be treated at a time. If I need four or five treatments for the breast/lymph, at six-week intervals, then it will be months before we can start on the lungs and liver. Hmmm.

I discussed this with my guru, Patricia. Obviously we have many other less conventional treatments which we are using. I take more vitamins and supplements than you can shake a stick at; I do lots of detoxing, as you know, and continuing the mind work and visualising, and I have the recent addition of Foxy, the oxygen machine.. All these are effective, but because they are relatively gentle treatments, they take time. Which is interesting.......... time I may, or may not, have.

Prof Vogl gave me information on some tablets which he says are very effective in conjunction with the targeted chemo. I have discussed these with Patricia. And we have decided that I should go ahead with them (in her words) "to keep me safe". I like that thought, it feels good. I went to hospital yesterday to discuss things with my oncologist, another Prof, (a female one, in this case). She also agreed. She is to get in touch with Prof Vogl to agree the dose, and subject to my blood tests being okay, I will commence the tablets on 13th May. These tablets are chemotherapy tablets, to halt the growth of the other tumours in my body, we hope. As they are in tablet form, I will be able to take them at home without lots of hospital visits. The side effects are what we know from chemo: sickness, tiredness, sore mouth, etc. The dose is gentler than IV chemo and, apparently, usually tolerated quite well, and I am unlikely to lose my hair. Apparently. So, that's all good.

In some ways, I feel disappointed that I need chemo after all. On the other hand, my gut instinct tells me that it is the right thing to do at this point.

The tic tacs are that I will stay on this for the next few months. I will sail through it, because I am physically up to it, and because I will carry on with everything else I am doing to look after my body and my health. I will come off it before it has had too much impact on my immune system. And then working with Patricia, BAM! We will start some other things to turbo boost my immune system to get it back where we need to be. And continue with the targeted chemo on the other tumours.

Good plan, huh? Foxy, in fact.

There are some other very important bits to Plan Foxy; that was just the update on the medical malarkey.

The most important bits are: to be happy. Now.

There are many ways to do this and I'm doing them already. I get grateful - remembering and noticing all the things, both big and small, that I am thankful for. I mix with people who make me laugh (thank you for last night, Rita, what a hoot). I have tulips in the kitchen. I listen to my favourite music too loud. I dress up (my Ascot dress got an outing this weekend; thank you, Jane). My friends who live away come and visit (thank you, Sonia, and Wendy, who comes up the M1 whenever she can). I cleared out all my old gold jewellery which I no longer wear, took it to a fabulous jewellers and came out with the prettiest diamond ring you have ever seen. Free diamonds! How fab is that?! (Thank you to Lucie and Julie). Need to book in to see Erica, and arrange a Chester Zoo trip with John, as they have a baby giraffe!!! Awwww!

I am also working on my bucket list to make those bigger things happen, and to have things in the diary to look forward to, which include: writing a book, a Sound of Music trip to Salzburg, more picnics (thank you, Laurane and Jackie), a vintage weekend to involve dressing up, more outings for my Ascot dress (thank you for the party invite, Jayne, and races invite, Julie), planning on moving house and having a new start back to my roots, and I fancy some new photos to use on my blog, Twitter and facebook, as I haven't got any up-to-date ones. Need more 'by the sea' adventure. I want to go to Alnmouth which looks sooo pretty. Also want to spend a week or two being horizontal in the sun… you get my drift.

*So! **Plan Foxy** is ready…everything is in place. What do I need from you? I need your encouragement, your friendship, surprises; I need you to be there for me.*

This can feel a lonely road sometimes, and it's easier and a lot more fun when someone is there to hold your hand, walk alongside you, lead the way, or give you a push from behind when you need it.

Ooh yes, and I also need you to work on your own bucket list. I love the idea of us all doing the things we have been meaning to do, or dreamed we might do... Let me know what you have planned. If you need rent-a-crowd to join in, I'm available!

****

Zapping Nummer Zwei – 4th May

What a difference six weeks can make. Six weeks ago I had my first targeted chemo treatment. A quick glance back to what was going on with me at that point:

I was in considerable discomfort, and sometimes, pain. I couldn't get comfortable when lying down, or forget for even a minute that I had cancer. Breathing was sometimes difficult and I had fluid on my lungs which made me cough, especially when lying down. Plus, I was extremely anxious that the Prof would take one look at my scans and send me home. All this tension was scrunched up in my neck and shoulders, causing me as much pain and discomfort as the cancer. It was in this state that I set off for my first treatment. Hardly surprising, then, that the trip was not a particularly fun one. Or that on my return, with the relief of having been treated, I collapsed into a very long sleep.

Fast forward six weeks; the treatment had done its stuff. The tumour under my arm in particular was noticeably smaller, making me much more comfortable. The fluid on my lungs had gone (although I did experience shortness of breath from time to time). Generally, I felt better, less tired, and could get comfortable enough to even lay on my right side which hadn't happened for a while. All in all, pretty damn good. So, as I set off to zap number two, I was in a very different place.

My friend, Jane, came with me. We decided to go out a day early, so that we could have a day playing out with the Frankfurters. So, we arrived on Tues evening. Wednesday was a beautiful spring day, as it was 1st May: a bank holiday in Germany. We strolled along the river to the Old Town soaking up the holiday atmosphere. When we had had enough exploring, we found a typical German eatery with big, long wooden tables and benches outside on the cobbled streets in the sunshine. We discovered how delish the local Apfelwein was. It's like a still, very dry cider. Yumscious. We lingered over lunch, chatting and soaking up that vitamin D. A lovely day.

Thursday was treatment day. Jane came to the hospital with me. I checked in and paid. When I went to the MRI reception we had a little confusion. She said

I had to bring 'her' and wait to be called. Who was 'her'? It turned out the receptionist didn't believe I was the patient and assumed I was checking someone else in. I liked that.

Jane toddled off to do her thing for the day while I did mine. MRI scan, then into the operating theatre; got all covered, prepped and drugged. The nurse asked me how I'd been and told me that I looked really well. It was lovely to get a compliment whilst laid out like a fish waiting to be filleted.

Then Herr Prof arrived. He asked how I was (fine, thanks), had I had any problems (no). Ready to rock n roll. He thought if he asked me about work that I wouldn't feel him slice into my groin and feed the catheter through. That was almost true. Pretty surreal to be chatting about the similarities and differences of the English and German legal and taxation systems, whilst he was doing all that. Made me smile.

Then to the recovery ward for three hours. I managed to sleep for a chunk of the time in between obs. The drips were removed, dressings checked, and I was allowed to get up. Feel fine. Off next for a CT scan then back to the Prof's waiting room where Jane was already waiting for me. It was good to see a friendly face and have someone to chat to. Eventually it was my turn to go in. He had a full screen of scans: mine from six weeks ago, and those from today. *Look* he says, clicking through with his remote control like boys do. I had no idea what these blobs were that I was looking at. *Look,* (click, click) *we are making good progress* (click, click). Me; fascinated, confused, looking. *Look, they are all getting smaller; here, look at the lungs.*

Lungs? Lungs! I said, 'Erm, can I stop you there?' He looked at me. 'Lungs? I didn't realise you were treating my lungs? I thought it was just the breast and lymph, here (I indicated my right side)'. He looked at me. *Yes, yes, of course we are. You will see on the scans. I will give you a CD with the before and after images. We are getting this under control; you just need to keep fighting.* 'I can do that,' I said. And with that, I was dismissed. He had other patients to see; he helps a lot of people.

I felt absolutely elated. It was working. I knew it was working, but it was great to hear Herr Prof say so. And to see the evidence. If only I understood it.

Jane and I practically skipped out of there into a lovely sunny evening. It was lovely to feel the fresh air after being in hospital all day. We strolled along the river for a while. I felt light and happy and optimistic. And lucky. Yes, lucky to be where I was.

Between Herr Prof, my oncologist here in Leeds (henceforth to be known as Lady Prof), who was now in touch with Herr Prof, to agree the dosage of the systemic chemo I was to start on 13th May, and my guru Patricia Peat of Cancer Options, who was working with me and would continue to after I finished treatment with Herr Prof – wow - what a team! And, of course, I had my family, my friends, and all of the people who had joined Team Nina.

That's what I meant by lucky. I felt loved, supported and as safe as any of us have the right to feel.

A Milestone Week - 19th May

It'd been a big week. It was now nine months since I was diagnosed with cancer. That is a long time when you have Stage 4 aggressive cancer. When you decide not to have chemotherapy and go unilateral. I wouldn't have dared to think too hard about how I would feel, and what would be going on for me nine months down the line. Or even to think that I would still be here.But here I was. Feeling better than I probably had any right to, and getting better all the time.

My maverick streak has always liked to do things a little differently, but never quite as much as now. In these nine months, I'd learned a lot: about cancer, about life, and most of all, about myself. I'd had lots of new experiences and firsts - some good, some not so good. I had totally changed my habits and lifestyle. I'd started a blog, had started to speak in public about my story, and started this book. And spent nearly seven weeks in total in Germany. So why was this particular week so important? Because it was the week I started systemic chemotherapy. If you've followed my story, you will know that this is not particularly where I wanted to be. But it's where I was, and it was just fine. As always, I'd got the information I needed to make an informed decision, and my instincts told me that it was absolutely the right thing to do at that point in time.

Since my last visit to the Lady Prof at Jimmy's, she had been in touch with Herr Prof to agree the correct dose of systemic chemo, alongside the targeted chemo treatment I was having in Frankfurt. In case you are not clear on the difference between the two: the targeted chemo goes directly to the tumours. This is good because the side effects are limited (or, in my case, practically non-existent). On the other hand, this does not reach the cancer I have elsewhere in my body; for example, in my bones. Hence the decision to have more general (systemic) chemo which goes into your system and travels throughout your body.

The chemotherapy I needed was in tablet form. My appointment on Monday was to start this course of treatment, or so I thought. After checking in at the breast clinic, I was off to the waiting room, armed with my cuppa (of green tea) and book - you never know just how long you will have to wait for your turn. You're called to be weighed whilst you wait, and they measure your height. This amuses me every time; it's doubtful I'd grown since the last time they measured me. When it was my turn to see the Lady Prof, she shakes my hand and says it was nice to see me, and that I was looking well. She examined me and agreed that there were signs of improvement since my Frankfurt treatment. We go through my blood results (I had called into hospital the week before to have some blood taken) - all was good.

My tumour markers were low last time, at 26, and have now dropped even further to 9. My kidney and liver function tests are normal; who ever thought I would be so delighted to achieve normal?! She listened to my breathing and acknowledged that it was better than previously. She asked if I would mind having a chest x-ray for her to check, and I agreed. She checked that I had read the information provided about the side-effects of the chemo, and that I was still happy to proceed, which I was. So gimme the tablets and let's get on with it, was what I thought. That is not what happened. She wrote me a prescription which I needed to take to the hospital pharmacy later on. A nurse popped in to tell me that my chemo pre-assessment appointment would be on Friday. Hrrrrmph. I thought THIS was my pre-assessment, let's-get-started-on-the-chemo-shall-we appointment. I asked if we couldn't-perhaps-maybe-do-this-right-now - today? No. Well, how about

Thursday then? Apparently not. I felt mildly irritated by this, because it felt inefficient and unnecessarily bureaucratic. Because I had built up that today was the day, and I wanted to get on with it. But mainly because on Friday, me and my gorgeous Ascot dress were supposed to be going to York Races with my friend, Julie. Just because I have cancer doesn't mean that I have nothing better to do, I thought. My time was as precious as anyone else's -perhaps even more so. But the hospital system doesn't really recognise that. So, Friday it is then. Back to Jimmy's. Again.

Julie had arranged to have the day off for the races, so she offered to come with me. It was good to have company. She asked some questions about what would happen at the appointment. I didn't know and we giggled about being 'Chemo Virgins'. We didn't have too long to wait before being called through. I was weighed and they wanted to do my height. Again. They also wanted to take some MRSA swabs. I wondered why this was, so I asked. Because we do for all chemo patients, she says. I asked, 'why is that?' She went out to check. It seemed that it was necessary if you come into hospital for IV chemo, but not in my case. So, no swabs.

A lovely nurse came in and introduced herself, and the medical student who was accompanying her. We went through all the necessary information

124

and questions; it was all chatty and informal. Which I
liked. I needed to take the tablets twice a day, twelve
hours apart. I may or may not suffer from the various
side effects, such as being susceptible to infection,
nausea, sore mouth, diarrhoea, sore hands and
feet. Oh, the glamour of it all. I was equipped with
anti-sickness and anti-diarrhoea tablets, mouthwash
and cream. I decide that I wouldn't be doing any
of that, and I would sail through it. I was to take my
first dose of tablets that evening, so that I could then
continue the twelve-hourly pattern easily: probably
7a.m./7p.m. I would take them for two weeks then
have a week off. I would come back to see Lady
Prof at the beginning of June to see how it had gone,
before my next Frankfurt trip. We left the hospital and
decided to hit the town. Cocktails in The Alchemist;
well, carrot and orange juice, actually. Shoe shopping.
Then lunch at Harvey Nicks. Chemo Day was an
awful lot better than I thought it would be! Thank
you, Julie, you're a star. She dropped me off at
home. I unpacked my shoes and beamed at them. I
unpacked my medicine cabinet of a carrier bag and
read all the instructions. The instructions on the chemo
tablets said: 'Medicine requires special monitoring. If
you are not the patient, handle with gloves.' So
you couldn't even touch this stuff. But it was okay
for me to swallow it. Charming. Don't mind me
then. The mouthwash was chlorohexidine gluconate.
Hmmm. Might stick with the oil pulling instead. The

aqueous cream looked okay. I found that the anti-diarrhoea tablets work by slowing down the speed of the movement of food through your bowel. I found that the anti-sickness tablets work by helping to move the food in your stomach through your digestive system more quickly. I kid you not. Imagine what would happen if you needed to take both at the same time. Hmmm. Let's hope I don't need to.

I prepared a meal as I needed to take the tablets with or after food, as they are too harsh on an empty stomach. Down the hatch. I am home alone. Wondering how I feel. If anything will happen. Deciding again that it won't. I went to sleep, wondering how I would feel when I woke up. I woke early. Remember the 'I Can' event that I spoke at in February? Well, today is the 'I Can, Event 2'. I had breakfast and took my second set of tablets. Was I feeling anything? No. I got dressed and went off to spend the day with Richard McCann, all the other speakers, my friends, Angela and Jayne, and numerous other people who were at the first event and who know my story, follow my blog, and were delighted to see and hear how well I was.

I met some new people and soaked up the positive vibes. I knew more than ever that I wanted to share my story and what I had learned so that I could make a difference. Incurable doesn't have to mean hopeless. You have choices. There are ways to prevent the chance of getting cancer, and of staying well when you have it - and I need to share this stuff. I resolved to seek out more speaking opportunities and spread the word. What a brilliant week. The next stage of the journey had begun. Hang on to your hats!

Chapter 8 – The Cancer Maverick

I have always called the daily regime I follow my 'Getting Better Every Day' plan, and that is exactly what I was doing. The targeted chemo did the trick. Each treatment had shrunk the tumours. I had eight treatments in all, between March and November. The systemic chemo didn't cause me any problems or side effects. I didn't need any anti-sickness, anti- diarrhoea, painkillers or any other medication. Now the chemo phase was over, I was starting hormone therapy, with the aim of halting or shrinking the tumours further. Again, I was not suffering side effects.

It hadn't all been totally good news, though. Cancer is a bit of a roller coaster. Just when you think you're on the up, something can happen to bring you back down with an almighty thud. It's strange what can trigger those downs. One of them for me was the death of Bernie Nolan at the beginning of July. I was surprised by how much it affected me, but it did. She'd had breast cancer, and it had returned and spread to her brain, lungs, liver and bones. She was the same age as me and was known for her positive attitude about it all. We had grown up together, so to speak. When she was 'In the Mood for Dancing', so was I. So, when she died, I somehow felt more vulnerable, that it could have been me, or that it could be me soon. The week it happened, as I went into the supermarket to stock up on veggies, I noticed her book for sale. *Now and Forever* by Bernie Nolan. I felt the need to know more. Was I really like her? Would it be happening to me soon? I bought the book and started reading it as soon as I got home; I couldn't put it down. I read as much as I could that day and finished it the day after.

My mind was put at rest; whilst I was sad about what had happened to her, it was apparent that we had very different views on our illnesses and how we approached staying well. I no longer felt that her destiny was mine. I could relax again.

Another big downer happened whilst I was on the systemic chemo. My blog tells the story:

26th September - Two steps forward and one step back – and I'm not talking salsa

If I thought about it, I could feel stressed. Maybe even very stressed. Which is not good for me.

All of a sudden my world's gone bonkers. I have accepted two speaking engagements at short notice. They each have very different requirements, so that means two lots of prep to do in not a lot of time. I have two speaking gigs coming up in October and November so they need some promotional blurb and photos, etc., and I have not yet got all this on file and ready, so that means more last minute admin. And I also have two big writing deadlines coming up: one for a magazine, one to contribute to a book. These are all things that I want to do but they are squished into a pretty small time frame.

I also have some social stuff going on. Thank goodness. But it does make me feel under a bit more time pressure. And what tends to give is the healthy living regime. I haven't got much in the fridge and I don't seem to have found time to shop. I keep running out of day! And I have the arrangements to make for my next Frankfurt trip, and Dad to visit, and a home to look after. You get my drift. I do wish I had a butler and housekeeper, and then I could concentrate on keeping well, which is getting very little of my attention at this time.

To top this all off, it's the time of the month when bills need paying. The amount of money I am going through on treatments is scary. Especially when you consider that it's at a time when I can't hold down a "proper job". Treatment seven next month; I wonder how many more I will need to pay for?

So what - we all have that, don't we? Work and family and home and money and life in general. This is true.

But, I guess what's at the bottom of it all, is that I have had some news I didn't want to hear. Which is on my mind and makes it harder to find the head space for the other stuff. The news is that the cancer has spread to my spine. I suspected those pesky bones might be a problem, which is why I agreed to go on systemic chemo as well as the targeted chemo.

This means that I now have to rethink my regime. I have doctors and hospital appointments to squeeze in, plus I am, of course, working with Patricia, my guru, to decide what we do next.

So, it's time for me to hit the 'pause button' again, I think. If I don't answer the phone or your emails, please bear with me. I need to take some time out, learn how to say no, get back in control of my life and decide on my game plan.

I am at the hospital on 7th October so will update you after that. Watch this space!

10th October - Ms Angry of Yorkshire

So, off I toddle to hospital AGAIN. Three weeks after my last appointment when I collected my chemo prescription. And Doctor Whateverhisnameis said they would be having an MDT meeting to decide my new treatment plan, now that the cancer has spread to my spine. I wasn't sure, therefore, whether I would be getting more chemo. Or, as Dr W had intimated, that

*they would propose putting me on hormone therapy
to shrink the tumours, together with bisphosphonate to
strengthen my bones. So I had psyched myself up to
hear what I needed to hear. That's what I thought was
going to happen, as that is what I'd been told..*

*I went for my 10.45 a.m. appointment, got weighed,
had some bloods taken and waited to see the doctor.
I was called in at about 12.15. By yet another different
doctor; let's call her Doctor Doesntknowmefromadam.
Apparently, Lady Prof wasn't in clinic. Like she wasn't
last time. I feel mildly irritated by this. I feel that I am at
a significant milestone in my treatment, and here I am
with a stranger who knows absolutely nothing about
me apart from the medical stuff written in my notes
that she has had to read through thoroughly before
calling me in. Hardly surprising that appointments run
behind schedule, methinks. They are so ripe for a spot
of business process re-engineering. I might do that
while I'm waiting around. I could charge the NHS; it
would help pay for my treatment in Germany.*

*She opens by telling me that there is no point in her
giving me a further chemo prescription as 'it clearly
isn't working'. Marvellous. Thanks for that. Just in case
I hadn't noticed, let's emphasise the negatives, eh?
She tells me that they can't decide anything further
about my treatment as they haven't had a response
from Herr Prof to the letter they sent to him, asking how*

many more sessions I will be having there.

This is all news to me; what letter? Why not send an email to save time? Why did I not know about this? I could have chased a response by phone or email. Come to think of it, why the hell am I here if I'm not having chemo or anything else? What happened in the MDT meeting, I ask. She looked at her screen. Mmmmmm, that hasn't happened. She doesn't know why. The reason my treatment plan can't be determined is because hormone therapy cannot be given whilst I am having chemo, even the targeted stuff. Strange that. Dr Whateverhisnameis knew at my last appointment that I was going to Frankfurt for more treatment on the 15th October, yet he still suggested that going on hormone therapy was the most likely cause of action. My confidence level in what I am being told is dropping by the second.

I tell her that I am extremely frustrated by the lack of continuity of care. (Amongst other things I'm not impressed with.)

She asks what I want to happen next. (She's asking me!?!) I said I thought I was coming to hear what my options are. In the absence of that, I ask for copies of the correspondence sent to my GP and to Herr Prof, and also the radiology report that was read out to me from the screen at my last appointment. She smiles, head on one side, saying that lots of patients don't want to know all this detail. My eyes opened quite wide at this point. I explained that as the information is about ME, I want to know everything. She clearly doesn't understand that the person in charge of my health is ME!

I am feeling very cross. It is now nine weeks since I provided copies of my scans and they are sending snail mail to Germany, whilst telling me in stark medical terms that this is pretty serious; "new thoracic spine metastatic disease".

I leave. After apologising to the doctor; although I am cross, it is not at her personally. She checks that Lady Prof will be in clinic for my next appointment, in two weeks' time.

I feel a big black cloud over my head. I need to get out of here.

That was Monday. Since then, I have cleansed myself of hospitalness and I am feeling much more balanced about it all.

I am delighted to not be on systemic chemo any more. I never wanted to be on it in the first place. I now need to get rid of the toxicity from my body. The 3E programme is brilliant for this. The crappocinos need to be a daily occurrence and I will do a liver cleanse in a few weeks.

I'm not too enthusiastic about the hormone therapy anyway, and going to the hospital is very bad for my wellbeing, so I may or may not persevere until I get a treatment plan, and I may choose not to follow it anyway. I will be working on my mental strength and especially on visualising. If you care to join in, that would be most welcome. I know that many of you pray for me - I like that. Even though I'm not religious, if you have strong belief then I absolutely know that those positive vibrations make a difference. So please, please carry on. And if you want to visualise my tumours melting like snow, and wishing me back to health, then that is very welcome too.

****

2014 – Aka the Year I might not have had

Generally though, life is good. Really good. I am living happily with my cancer, and it doesn't stopping me living my life. I have a few hospital visits to fit into my schedule, some medication to take, and my daily 'Getting Better Every Day' regime to follow. I am much more chilled out about it all. I know how to do this now. Which means that I have the time and energy for other things. I needed a focus, things to achieve but - mindful of the things I had learned at the 3E Centre - it needed to be something that would enhance my life and not give me stress and worry. The reaction from my blog has been great and the feedback from my speaking had been really touching. I like being a Cancer Maverick and showing that having incurable cancer isn't the end of the world. Life can carry on – this seems to be my mantra.

I decided to speak using my first and middle names, Nina Joy. My niece (with a degree in advertising and marketing) took over, getting me re-branded, and developing my blog into a website to showcase me as a speaker. The bookings started to come through. Cancer elicits powerful emotion from an audience, which is what moves people to make changes. Cancer also provides some useful and thought-provoking analogies which provide parallels when thinking about how to tackle issues in life and in business.

Although it's important to talk about cancer, I enjoy speaking to business audiences. After all, I have much more experience in business than I do at having cancer!

The final cherry on my 2013 cake was starting to write this book. I have loved books and reading all my life. It has been a lifelong ambition to write a book, to see my name on a book in a bookshop. I never knew what to write about but the universe seemed to have something in mind. All in all, it's been quite a year! My blog posts tell the tale…

It's been a doozie! - 30th December 2013

2013, that is. It's had some serious downs and some rather lovely ups. At this time of year, I like to look back on what happened, what I've achieved, and what I've learned,

So, let's see - what happened? At the start of the year it was four months into my cancer story. I was doing lots of things to look after myself, and although my healthy cells appreciated it, the cancer was too advanced and carried on growing. I was getting increasingly ill..

In February, I appeared at Richard McCann's I Can event, speaking in public for the first time about my experiences. It felt good, and I wanted to do more. Unfortunately though, I continued deteriorating. By my birthday in March there was no getting away from the fact that I was ill. I was awarded my Disabled badge - which I needed. I had fluid on my lungs and couldn't walk very far without getting out of breath. My breast and arm were extremely uncomfortable; I couldn't lay on my left hand side or front, and had restricted movement. It is no exaggeration to say that I didn't think I would see my next birthday if I carried on at this rate.

But then everything changed. I found Patricia Peat of Cancer Options. I was referred to Herr Prof in Frankfurt for the targeted chemotherapy. I had my first treatment at the end of March which was the beginning of my comeback. I started to feel better straight away, although I continued treatment throughout the year until November. I also had systemic chemo here in the UK between May and Sept/Oct. I sailed through it all. I didn't feel ill, or look ill, or need to take painkillers. Not what you expect from someone with Stage 4 cancer really, is it? Usually, it's all downhill.

I went on holiday with my sis in July, and I remember lying in the sun, and feeling for the first time in an age that there wasn't anything wrong with me. Physically, that is. I decided to take most of August off, and I enjoyed the wonderful English summer being outdoors as much as I could. I had the tan to prove it.

As I was feeling so well, I was able to turn my attention to what I now want to do with my life. And that is to continue what I started with this blog - sharing what I'm learning so that it can help and give hope to others in my situation. And my new Nina Joy branding and website, and Nina Joy Facebook page were launched to spread the word. But I'm not just about cancer. I also use what I learn to inspire businesses to do more, too. In the latter part of 2013 I did a number of speaking bookings, and I already have a number of bookings for 2014.

I have also written (well, almost) my first book, telling my story. The plan is to have it published in January, so *look out, world, Nina Joy the author is a-comin'!*

All in all, a pretty spectacular year, considering how it looked at the start. I am feeling all sorts of emotions about it. Definitely lucky. Also a little bemused: how can this happen for me, and yet many others like me are not here to tell the tale? That makes me sad. But all I can do is carry on what I'm doing, share what I learn, and hope that it benefits others, too.

Thank you so much to all of you for the comments you leave for me - I love it when you do. And also for the millions of other things that help me, especially the belief and positive vibes and prayers and wishes. Please carry on doing so. It can seem that I'm fine, even that I'm 'cured'. But I'm not - we still have work to do in 2014, so I hope you stick with me.

I am really looking forward to next year, and am setting myself some humungously exciting goals. More of that in the next blog post, methinks.

I hope you review your own year. Celebrate the successes and achievements. See if you can learn anything from the rest. And let's get excited about a whole new, very precious year coming up.

2014 – A new year, and one I may not have seen...

Hello, lovely people. Let me apologise for being so late with my New Year blog. I do have a great excuse, though. I have been putting all my writing energies into my book. And I am delighted to say that I have finished the first draft! I am now awaiting feedback from my book coach - maybe it will need a lot more re-working. Hopefully it won't - will keep you posted on developments.

I thought I would share with you my goals for 2014. It seems quite a strange concept, doesn't it - someone who is supposedly terminally ill having goals. Well, I have.. When I was first diagnosed it was hard to look forward, but I've realised how much it helps me. As well as enjoying today, and planning for tomorrow, it's great to have things further in the future to work towards. If the worst came to the worst, those plans may have to be amended - but we can cross that bridge if and when we come to it, can't we?

My goals are (in no particular order):

1. Stay alive and well

2. Publish my book

3. Build my speaking business

4. Fall in love

5. Be by the sea more and/or in the sun

6. Get fitter

7. Write more books

That should do for starters. If my year had all of those things in it I would be one very happy bunny. If you can help me with any of these, please do; I could do with all the help I can get!

My diary is starting to fill up quite nicely with some exciting jaunts, but there)s room for more...............watch this space. I will probably be blogging a bit more now the book's finished, although I suppose that depends on the level of rewriting that)s needed.........

If there is anything in particular you want to know more about, just let me know. If not, you will just have to put up with my ramblings :-)

****

It all sounds rather marvellous doesn't it? I feel incredibly lucky. Blessed even, and that is not a word that I use lightly. It feels as though this was all meant to happen, I don't really know why. Yet. I feel as though I've achieved quite a lot at a time when I might not have been expected to do so. I like that.

I am not the same person I was before cancer came crashing into my life.

I feel much more vulnerable. That is not necessarily a bad thing. My emotions are much closer to the surface. I can cry at the drop of a hat – because I'm happy, or sad, or just moved – I never used to be like that.

I have also learned so much – about cancer,

about myself, about life. I have learned that the person who is responsible for my health is me. Doh! I wish this had clicked with me years ago – I might not have been in this position. We depend far too much on the NHS and allow it to take the responsibility we should take ourselves. Let me give you an example: breast screening in this country starts at age 50. I therefore was waiting patiently to be called. But if I had any concerns that I might get breast cancer one day (I did), then why, oh why, did I not decide to have screening earlier by paying for it myself?! We don't spend money on such things, do we? We just wait for the NHS to do its stuff. It might seem an expense but trust me, it's a snip compared to the financial impact of having cancer.

What else have I learned? That cancer doesn't just happen to you; it has a ripple effect on those around you. The closer they are, the bigger the impact. Friends, and even acquaintances, are affected. Sometimes, in a good way – a number of people in Team Nina have done things they might not have got round to doing because what's happening to me is a massive wake up call.

I have learned that cancer is a word that scares people. Some of the people who were in my life have been less present in my life since my diagnosis. Cancer isn't catching, but it does remind people of their own mortality. And because I have incurable cancer, it raises the spectre of death and loss and some wish to protect themselves from that by loosening their connection to you. Hey – we all do what we need to do.

Looking back, do I wish I had done things differently? Absolutely not.

I am absolutely convinced that I have done the right things – for me. The route I have taken isn't for everyone. It's lonely being a maverick, having the courage to follow your instincts, going against the norm. It has been eye-wateringly expensive – good job I'm worth it (to be said in the L'Oreal ad voice). And not everyone would be prepared to make massive lifestyle changes at a time when you have less energy and resources. I've always liked change, though – it suits my concentration span (which is that of a gnat).

When you are diagnosed with incurable cancer, the last thing people expect you to do is to wait seven months before starting (conventional) treatment. I did my 3E education first, and that I believe has been the foundation on which everything else has worked. That is why the targeted chemo had such a good effect. It isn't a miracle cure for everyone: we saw a lady in Frankfurt on my very first visit. She looked very ill and frail. I felt ill, but nothing like as bad as she clearly was. Several months later, back in Frankfurt, I was really well by this point, laughing and chatting with my sister. We saw this lady again, and she looked even more frail and delicate. Why was I so lucky, and so different, we wondered?

I took systemic chemo for a few months, and sailed through it. The anti-sickness and anti-diarrhoea pills and antiseptic mouthwash gathered cobwebs. Again, why was I so lucky, and so different?

I believe that my 3E regime made the difference, especially on my mental strength. Everything that I have done subsequently has added to that, and helped me to get better and better.

When I started out on this adventure, I genuinely believed that I could be cured - that I could cure myself. I've changed my views on that in light of my experiences. But that doesn't mean I have given up. Hell, no. I always felt that my body had made this cancer, not that it was a horrendous foreign body that had to be hacked or nuked away. I used to think that you had to get rid of the cancer and be cured, or succumb to it and die. I've learned that that's not necessarily the case. It seems that my cancer and I can happily co-exist. Who knew?

So, what does the future hold?

More speaking, I think; possibly more books. Lots of love and laughter, happiness and experiences,

I hope.

Medically, who knows? I can't control that. I don't sit worrying about it all the time either. Whatever happens, when it happens, I will consult my experts, decide what the best course of action is for me, and then go for it.

I do know that I don't ever want anyone to say those words about me that we hear so often when someone dies, that they have 'lost their battle with cancer'. Firstly, I don't see it as a battle. And I hate the idea of losing. Everyone has to die of something, don't they? We don't say of someone in a car accident that they 'lost their battle with a lorry', do we?

It feels strange talking about dying. I don't feel as though I am. Maybe I will be around for quite some time yet, maybe I won't. I don't want to be arrogant enough to presume I've got this licked.

Whatever happens, I feel that it's a happy ending. I'm very lucky that I have had chance to squeeze a bit more out of life than I might have been expected to, following my diagnosis. Life truly is what you make it.

To be continued ...

Acknowledgements

- My sister, Julie; bro-in-law, David; niece Lucie and nephew James – couldn't do all this without you. Life is more fun with you in it.

- Oscar Dog, for being utterly inspirational in the tumour-disappearing department

- Wendy, for being my friend since the beginning of time

- Andy, for your practical advice and unending support

- Team Nina – all the people who follow me on Twitter, my blog and my facebook page – your good wishes and positive vibes really do make a difference

- My medical team – the two Profs and Patricia, my guru. Thank you for doing what you do; I wouldn't be here without your expertise.

- Everyone at the 3E Zentrum – it all started with you; I wouldn't be here today without you

- Yes to Life – without you I wouldn't have found Patricia Peat of Cancer Options, and Herr Prof

About the Author

Nina is proud to be Yorkshire born and bred, and now lives in Leeds.

She has always believed in having a positive approach and remembers her dad teaching her very early on in life, that 'you can if you think you can'.

Her belief in positivity and getting through tough times has been tested, but luckily Nina loves a challenge. She feels that she has been training for this all her life, and she's used everything she has learned personally and professionally to get where she is today. Nina wants to share her experience of what could be a hopeless situation to show others that this is not necessarily so.

As a professional speaker, Nina now shares her story with business audiences and other groups. She believes that we can all achieve more than we think we can, and challenges audiences to do just that.

To keep up with Nina's story, or to get in touch:

Website - Ninajoy.com

Email - hello@ninajoy.com

Twitter - @ninajoy1

facebook/Ninajoyspeaker